FIGHTING BACK

Elizabeth Reilly

Matador
9 Priory Business Park
Kibworth Beauchamp
Leicestershire LE8 0RX, UK
Tel: (+44) 116 279 2299
Fax: (+44) 116 279 2277
Email: books@troubador.co.uk
Web: www.troubador.co.uk/matador

ISBN 978-1783062-225

British Library Cataloguing in Publication Data.
A catalogue record for this book is available from the British Library.

Typeset in Aldine by Troubador Publishing Ltd
Printed and bound in the UK by TJ International, Padstow, Cornwall

Matador is an imprint of Troubador Publishing Ltd

For Ed
for his unfailing patience, support and love throughout the bad times,
and for
Dr Chris Parsons
who turned my life around.

About the Author

Elizabeth Reilly was born in Berkshire. After studying at the Royal Academy of Music she worked briefly as a secretary at the BBC before embarking on a career of teaching music and piano in Hertfordshire, London and Surrey. In 2004, nearing retirement, she moved to Gloucestershire with her second husband. She has a grown-up daughter and son from her first marriage. Her interests include walking, gardening, reading and playing and listening to music.

"Life is what happens to you while you're busy making other plans"

John Lennon: *Beautiful Boy*

"Chronic pain is a world unto itself...Pain is supposed to be a warning to tell our brains that there is a problem needing to be corrected. Chronic pain, however, becomes the problem in and of itself. Acute pain protects life. Chronic pain destroys it"

Devin J. Starlanyl and Mary Ellen Copeland: *Fibromyalgia and Chronic Myofascial Pain (Second Edition)*

Some names in the text have been changed.

Contents

Muscles of the hip – anterior view

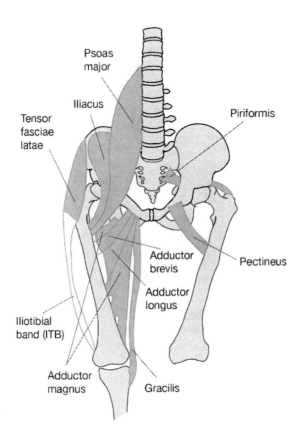

Psoas major

Iliacus

Tensor fasciae latae

Piriformis

Adductor brevis

Pectineus

Adductor longus

Iliotibial band (ITB)

Adductor magnus

Gracilis

Some of the structures referred to in the text – posterior view

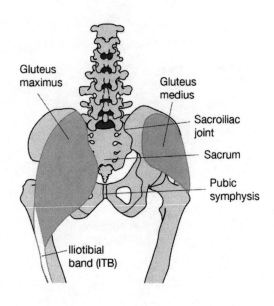

Introduction

I'm never happier than on a bright sunny day donning my walking boots and taking to the hills. With a map, a bottle of water and a few sandwiches and with the countryside opening up before me I can keep going for hours. Or at least I could, once upon a time.

This story starts at the end of 2004 when I and my partner, now husband, Ed, moved to Gloucestershire to walk in the Cotswolds, the Malverns and all the surrounding countryside. We joined the Ramblers and throughout the early part of 2005 enjoyed some wonderful walks, reaping what we had sown, after two years of hunting for our ideal retirement location. Discovering our new area with its many beautiful hills, valleys and villages, and maintaining and developing the large garden we had acquired were intended to keep me out of mischief for many years to come. So it was a cruel twist of fate when the following July, seven months after moving, a seemingly trivial accident threatened to deprive me of the very things I had moved for.

Well I wasn't going to be deprived of them – not without a fight anyway. To start with I trusted the professionals to "fix" me. But when that didn't happen I had to become more pro-active in trying to learn and understand what my problems were so that I could seek out the most beneficial treatments and practitioners for myself. I had no idea it would be such a long haul. As soon as one problem was sorted out it seemed that another surfaced. It felt like those Russian dolls that you lift up only to discover another one inside.

I started from a position of complete ignorance. I don't think I could have named a single muscle in my body. I knew hardly anything about joints or cartilage, nothing about ligaments, and I'd certainly never heard of connective tissue, or people called "musculoskeletal specialists". In my new Gloucestershire home I had set up a part-time piano teaching practice, and was free at last from classrooms in which I had spent many not very happy years. But while I could happily prepare pupils for their graded piano exams I couldn't have passed a Grade 1 equivalent – not even the Prep Test – in any kind of anatomy. Looking back I am appalled at my ignorance. But I don't think I'm alone. I simply hadn't been taught this stuff at school – although they did teach me about the digestive system of a rabbit – and I'd had no cause to learn any of it in all the intervening years since. If I was to get the answers I needed I had to negotiate a very steep learning curve.

I had many excellent therapists along the way, but for the first four years there was no one person who drew the threads of everything together. I longed for an overall project manager. Part of the problem lay in the nature of pain itself. It was incredibly difficult to describe in a meaningful way every single pain, of which I had many, to another person. No matter how well qualified and experienced my practitioners were in their own fields, or how empathic, I couldn't make them *feel* what my body was feeling. It was *my* pain – only I experienced it. I had to become my own project manager.

Chronic pain is extremely debilitating. Day after day after week after month it is exhausting and even the most resilient people – of whom I am not one – can be worn down by it. But I was driven by a seething frustration at the limitations now imposed so arbitrarily on my life, and the total bewilderment of not understanding what had happened to me. And so, in addition to all the people I saw, I spent hours on the internet, bought and read self-help books, and wrote a "pain diary" that extended into hundreds of pages, till I had inched my way towards understanding.

Although I sometimes felt I saw too many people and sometimes got contradictory advice I always learned something new from the different professionals I saw and gradually this enabled me to build up a picture over time. In some cases a chance remark set me off researching in a new direction, until finally I saw the right person who helped it all make sense. And even then there was a long way to go before I had "cured" my pain, or at least reduced it to a tolerable level.

I am aware of course that other people's ailments come pretty low down the scale of engaging topics. In the early days family and friends would kindly ask me how I was feeling, only to regret it when I told them. Eventually they stopped asking altogether. Although I've tried not to dwell on pain you can take it as read that it was there as a constant unless I specifically state otherwise. This is my story giving an account of the challenges I faced and the detective work I had to do to get my answers.

CHAPTER 1

An Unusual Injury

The Accident and First Physiotherapy

The weather was kind in 2005 as we adapted to life in the Gloucestershire countryside. In the spring we worked happily setting up our new garden, experiencing the excitement of Gold Cup week as crowds flocked to Cheltenham and helicopters buzzed constantly overhead. We enjoyed days out to Gloucester Cathedral and docks and to the Three Counties Show in its spectacular site at the foot of the Malvern Hills. We got married in May and had a lovely family weekend. And we indulged our passion for walking, sometimes with the Ramblers, sometimes alone, revelling in the scenery and congratulating ourselves on moving to such a stunning location. Our retirement plans, it seemed, were coming to fruition in a manner I hadn't dared hope for.

Even the one big worry that I'd brought to Gloucestershire with me – what to do about my elderly mother – had been solved by the end of June. Aged 91 and fiercely independent she had been living alone in a bungalow in Sussex. But it was no longer fair to expect agency carers and kind neighbours to cope with her general frailty and memory loss, and I'd been desperate to move her from the moment we'd been settled. Eventually my brothers and I got her into residential care just over two miles from my new home, where she was well looked after for the next three years.

I was worried about whether she would settle happily, given the resistance she'd put up to living in a "home", and moving day had proved fairly traumatic. I visited daily to start with and on the third day found her sitting in the residents' lounge reading the Telegraph and looking cheerful and well.

"How nice to find you in here," I said, *rather than skulking in your room.*

"Why shouldn't I sit here? It's for everybody you know – it's a nice place to sit."

"Oh yes it is. How long do you think you've been living here?"

"Oh at least a week, perhaps more."

I breathed a huge sigh of relief and dared to miss a day. Then I cut it down to three days a week, a schedule I kept up for nearly two years.

June turned into July and the weather was glorious. Ed and I had regular evening walks after the heat of the day, discovering all our local footpaths and getting to know our new territory. What a joy it was to be able to walk from our front gate and be in beautiful countryside straight away! I was at last beginning to relax after the stress of moving my mother and it seemed there wasn't a cloud on the horizon.

On the evening of July 6th, discovering yet another new footpath, we were climbing up a hill stopping frequently to look back at the view. The hillside was dotted with sheep contentedly grazing; below us were the roofs of houses giving way to a broad panorama of fields beyond, and behind it all was the backdrop of the Malvern Hills seen against the evening light. It was a wonderful sight and I breathed a huge sigh of contentment. I couldn't have been more at peace with the world.

We were chatting happily together as we approached a stile beside a padlocked gate. Ed stood aside to let me go over it first – he's such a gentleman, you see. I climbed onto the stile and then put my right leg over the top of the fence. As I was transferring my weight from my left foot to my right the whole structure wobbled then fell away to the left and my foot skidded off to the right, leaving me doing the splits across the fence. At least I think that's what happened. Did I fall to the ground? I don't know. Was I half-twisted talking to Ed behind me? Again I don't know. I do know I said to him "Watch that, it's very wobbly" and he came over safely. It seems crazy that even the following day I could scarcely remember the exact sequence of events, but at the time I didn't think to take particular note as nothing hurt and I was sure I'd not damaged myself in any way. We continued the half-mile or so home with no further problems.

The next morning I woke up and couldn't walk. I didn't know it then, but my life – at the age of fifty five – had changed forever. It's a day I shall not easily forget as it was also the day of the 7/7 bombings in London.

I had severe pain in my right groin and down the inside of my right thigh. It was a recurrence, I thought, of an injury I'd sustained three and a half-years previously when I was still living on the outskirts of London. I'd woken up one day with pain in my groin and inner thigh without knowing what had caused it. I could only assume that I had strained something at the gym where I was trying to improve my fitness before going ski-ing. My GP diagnosed strained adductor (inner thigh) muscles, aka groin strain, and recommended anti-inflammatories, rest and physiotherapy. After three sessions of deep heat and ultrasound from a physio I was better and went off to fly down the Austrian ski-slopes without a further thought about it.

Now, three and a half years later, I assumed I'd re-injured the adductors again. There didn't seem any point in going to the GP, who, at this stage, I barely knew. I took painkillers, rested as much as I could and phoned a physiotherapy clinic in the next village. They were booked up for the whole week but I managed to get an appointment straight away at a larger practice in Cheltenham. The physio there put my leg through a series of movements, I said "ouch" appropriately and she agreed with my diagnosis of adductor strain. Out came the heat and ultrasonic machines and I was given exercises to do at home. I had three or four sessions with more or less the same regime and I did my exercises religiously. I also applied hot towels and ice to my groin for weeks, till I became sick of the sight of soggy towels and dripping plastic bags festooning the bathroom.

I didn't get any better. I got worse. By now I had visited my new GP who had prescribed 600mg of ibuprofen to be taken three times a day. 1800 mgs for a woman of five foot two, albeit a slightly overweight one, is a large dose. Even that didn't seem to make much difference.

I told myself I was doing too much as indeed I was. But I was committed to being busy for a few more weeks yet. I drove the four-hour journey to Sussex and made a start on clearing and cleaning my mother's bungalow, a task my brothers would later complete. Whilst there I climbed a ladder, which can hardly have helped things, to prune some overgrown pyracantha, but I wanted to stop the property advertising itself as empty.

I also prepared for a house warming party for my extended family planned since May. I worked hard for it and it went well, although it poured with rain all day, and my vision of everyone lounging in T-shirts on the lawn vanished, as twenty people ranging from my one-year-old great-nephew to my ninety-one-year-old mother crowded into our small sitting room while the rain beat down on the windows outside. Several members of the family camped in the orchard area at the back of our garden and others stayed in the local b. and b. and the partying continued on the Sunday.

We were going on holiday after that and this was when I told myself I would finally rest. We'd planned a motoring tour of Scotland – Ed's home country – with some walking thrown in, and I reckoned that I could limit the walking and that the long periods in the car would finally give my leg the chance it needed to rest. Rest, I was sure, was what I needed. At least the fabulous scenery and the glorious weather – yes, even in Scotland – made up for the pain. In fifteen days we had only one and a half days of rain. We drove all round the west and north coasts of Scotland, with more and more breathtaking views round every corner.

But my pain did not improve. One day I was feeling really low as I struggled to walk round the streets of Thurso. We went to a chemist where the pharmacist told me I could take paracetamol as well as ibuprofen since they worked in completely different ways, and sold me a Tubigrip and a tube of Deep Heat muscle rub. The latter was ineffective, but the Tubigrip helped give my thigh a bit of support and I started guzzling even more pills till I rattled.

I was walking more and more awkwardly in order to avoid the pain in my groin. It seemed to be radiating out in all directions from this point and I was starting to waddle in order to walk at all. I was also beginning to get bad backache. Towards the end of the holiday when we were staying with some old friends of Ed's I was suddenly aware of something like an electric shock going down the back of my leg. As this continued to come in waves I wondered if it was sciatica – something I'd only vaguely heard of. Whilst I contemplated this new rather scary sensation, my phone, silent all holiday until now, rang shrilly. It was a carer from the residential home back in Gloucestershire; my mother had had a fall and been taken to hospital for X-ray, where they'd found she'd cracked her pelvis in two places. Life was beginning to get complicated.

One of my brothers heroically drove from Suffolk to Gloucestershire and back again on August Bank Holiday Monday to see Mum and reassure the family that she was being taken care of. She was. She was in the best place possible. I was due back home on the train on Tuesday, leaving Ed to spend a further week in Scotland with the car, looking up old friends and visiting old haunts. I didn't want to interrupt his plans since in normal circumstances I could exist perfectly well without a car for a week.

Once home I spent the next week trying to rest and taking taxis to the care home to visit Mum. Surgery on her pelvis had been ruled out because of her age and frailty. She had been transferred to the nursing floor of the home and given bed rest and strong painkillers which made her sleep most of the time. After three or four days she started physiotherapy and was encouraged gently to mobilise with a Zimmer frame. She was clearly in severe pain and it was heart-breaking to see her struggles. Nevertheless the approach was the right one because gradually, day by day, she improved and after a month went back to her old room. By Christmas she had no pain at all and had completely forgotten that she'd ever had a fall or gone to hospital or lived in another room for a month. There are advantages to memory loss!

"These things are marvellous!" she said of the Zimmer frame which she was never without now, and I smiled wryly remembering her scornful comment, "I'll never have one of those!" when she'd first moved and seen other residents with them.

My own pain, however, had not improved. When Ed arrived back from Scotland with the car I booked myself in for more physiotherapy. I wanted a second opinion and this time was able to get an appointment at the village clinic. Here I saw a delightful bubbly woman in her thirties called Linda. Again I told my story, adding in that I now had back pain and sciatica. Linda concentrated her attentions on my back and from her I learned about "lumbar vertebrae" and "facet joints" – joints which help support the weight and control movement between the individual vertebrae of the spine. She mobilised these joints, which she said were very stiff, and used ultrasound on them. There was no doubt my back was hurting badly, but it was my groin I'd injured – what was going on? Linda said it could be pain "referring" from my back. She sold me a lumbar roll and gave me more exercises to do, this time curling up with my knees to my chest and rocking gently. I had a further visit to the GP who added a drug called amitriptyline to my large daily dosage of pills. It had muscle-relaxing properties and would, he said, help me to sleep, as sciatica did not respond to normal painkillers.

Linda's diagnosis of stiff facet joints may have been accurate, but it was only a small part of the story and I didn't feel I was getting any better. I decided I'd just got to try something else. Not only was my groin pain still severe, my back was now extremely bad. All I wanted to do was lie flat out on the sofa all day. There are people called osteopaths and chiropractors, I thought. They fix backs, don't they? I was only vaguely aware of such people and hadn't a clue what they did. I looked up my "Complete Family Health" book, which had a section on complementary therapies at the back and read up about osteopathy and chiropractic. I didn't really take in most of it but did remember this scary-sounding thing called a "high velocity thrust" in which your joints would crack and pop. It sounded terrifying! But then I saw a brief section on McTimoney chiropractic, which was, the book said, a gentler version and I decided I would give that a try. I had to try something. I looked up Yellow Pages and found to my astonishment that there was a McTimoney chiropractic practice in the next village. On 29th September I attended my first chiropractic appointment with Meg. It was to be the start of a very long relationship with my local Natural Health Centre.

CHAPTER 2

Straightening Up

The Chiropractors

Meg took a complete medical history and also asked me how much medication I took. She raised her eyebrows when I said I was on 1800 milligrams of ibuprofen a day. She then asked me to rate my pain on a scale of 1-10. How on earth do you do that, I wondered? I didn't know where to begin, but it became clear she wasn't going to budge until she'd got an answer. My pain was bad, definitely. Assuming that nought was no pain at all and ten was the point at which you passed out I fished around and said, "about six or seven."

"Even with all that medication?"

"Yes."

She raised her eyebrows again, but said nothing.

Then it was time for an examination. She said my pelvis was very out of alignment, which she ascribed to walking awkwardly because of the groin pain. My pelvis? I didn't know anything about pelvises other than that Elvis had had one which he'd used to very good effect. I certainly didn't know they could get misaligned. What Meg was saying though seemed to make sense. The pelvis is the foundation for supporting the whole of the upper body and it's clear it needs to be properly balanced and stable.

Meg then started the treatment. To my surprise the "adjustments" as she called them were so quick that I felt nothing at all. She said I would need about six sessions, booked me up for the following week and told me to do pelvic floor exercises. Six sessions seemed a lot – little did I know then that it would only be a beginning!

My appointment had been on a Thursday. By Saturday I was feeling quite a lot better. By Monday I had hardly any pain at all and the sciatica had gone. I'd found something which really worked! I went with Ed to the Gloucestershire and Warwickshire steam railway where he was having a "Driving Experience" day, an overdue birthday present from me. I was invited to climb up into the engine driver's cab. I knew it was a mistake but I did it and it was almost worth it. By Thursday most of my pain had come back.

"That's common," Meg reassured me at my next session. "Don't worry, your pelvis will stabilise in time."

In this session I began to learn new terms. "Sacroiliac joint" was one of them. The sacroiliac joints (SIJs) join the sacrum – the part of the pelvis at the bottom of the spine – to the larger bony structures that form the sides of the pelvis – the ilia. My right SIJ was "out" – part of my pelvis had slipped up and was sitting high. In the months and years to come I was to hear a lot about SIJs in general and mine in particular.

"Piriformis" was another term. The piriformis is a muscle deep in your bum. Mine was very tight and "piriformis syndrome", I learned, was a classic cause of sciatica as this muscle, when tight, can trap the sciatic nerve. In fact all my muscles were very tight. "What you'd really benefit from,"

Meg said, "would be a massage. If you had one before next week I'd be able to get in a bit deeper."

It sounds naïve to say I knew nothing about massage but I really didn't. I thought it was something that people with more money than sense had to pamper themselves. However, I was beginning to think that Meg was doing me a lot of good, and if she recommended massage then massage I would have. There was a massage therapist at the same clinic and I booked a session with her the following week followed by a third chiropractic treatment the day after.

I began to look forward to it. A massage, I thought, what a lovely treat! It wasn't; it was unbelievably painful. I felt I was being run over by a bus. Everything was topsy-turvy – the chiropractic which I'd dreaded so much didn't trouble me at all, while this eagerly anticipated massage was proving to be hell. And my left side was as tight as the right – why was this? Kim, the massage therapist, commented on the tightness of all my muscles but unfortunately didn't recommend that I have any more sessions with her and being ignorant I thought that one was all I needed.

After my third chiropractic session we went on a walking weekend with the Ramblers in Shropshire. There was no way I could ramble now, but the trip had been booked and paid for in April when I was fit and well. On Saturday morning in our hotel room I tried out the new exercise which Meg had given me, adding to the repertoire I was slowly building up. This one was for stretching my piriformis. Lying on my back I put my right leg over my left one and pulled it across. It sent strong pains down my groin, which lasted for the rest of the week. My back also became very bad again. I spent most of the rest of the day – a depressingly foggy one – lying on the bed and distracting myself by reading "Coastliners" by Joanne Harris, which totally gripped me. I also fitted in a sauna. Meg had said it would do me good, but I didn't notice that it made any difference. Did I really expect a bit of hot steam to cure severe pain? I don't know, but since the hotel was offering saunas it seemed worth trying anything!

On Sunday afternoon when the weather was better I drove over the Long Mynd and then parked in the beautiful Carding Mill Valley, where I had walked with a friend thirty-two years previously. The sun was out and the autumn colours were glorious. I continued to read here, lying flat on my back on the ground, until the walking party appeared and I joined them for tea in the cafe. What with that and the conviviality of the group in the evenings I got something out of the weekend.

October and November went by and I completed my six chiropractic sessions. Meg was pleased with my progress and said my pelvis was almost straight and she spaced the sessions further apart. I, however, was less convinced. I would feel improvement after the sessions but sooner or later I would get pain again somewhere – in my back, in my groin, and in my right thigh which sometimes went into spasm and felt as if it was encased in concrete. I found I could reduce this by wearing an insole in my shoe, as it enabled the leg to work less hard.

Meg was sure I was improving and was encouraging me to get moving. She added in a "bicycling" movement to my exercises, told me to take two short walks a day and suggested I should also try swimming. Swimming didn't seem to make me either better or worse until the 20th November when, after trying out my bicycling exercises in the pool, I sent severe pains down my groin again. It was the last time I would swim for eighteen months.

I was getting depressed and went back to my GP, who said he would refer me for an X-ray on my hip. A hip problem, he said, was the first thing that would need to be ruled out if he was to refer me to an orthopaedic specialist. Regarding daily life, "Continue to potter," he said. I stared at him. I didn't want to potter. I wanted my life back. Not so long ago I'd had a life where I'd juggled full-time work, family, domestic chores, ageing parents, playing tennis and learning German – a life in which I'd once done six things before breakfast. Now at the very least I wanted to be able to walk across a room without pain – and I couldn't.

On 1st December I saw Meg for the seventh time. I updated her on everything – the GP visit, the referral for X-ray and the pain on swimming.

"It hurts so much here," I wailed, pointing right to the middle of my pelvis in the front. Her eyes lit up, I swear they did.

"You could have pubic symphysis dysfunction," she said.

"What?"

"Pubic symphysis dysfunction."

The pubic symphysis (PS), she explained, is where the pelvis meets at the front. It's not a part of the body that one would normally go round talking about! But as mine was injured I had to learn to talk about it, so you'll just have to get used to it. It seemed that the right side of mine was sitting higher than the left – what Meg termed right superiority. Basically I was coming apart in the middle. She leaned on the right half of my pubic bone and pressed swiftly and hard – at least that's what I think she did. "You'll feel sore for a bit," she said. "Go home and put ice on this." I would not see her again until after Christmas.

The following day I had no pain at all! Anywhere! I went round all day saying "Meg has caused a miracle, Meg has caused a miracle!" Two days later I was in agonies again. The adjustment hadn't lasted.

Meg had told me not to wear an insole – it would only discourage the pelvis from stabilising and the muscles in the right leg from stretching. The spasm would go eventually, she said. But it was my body not hers, and I would do anything to get pain relief. I was learning to manage things with a combination of medication, ice, heat packs, hot baths, insole, rest and gentle exercises and things would gradually improve until something else would set the whole pain cycle off again.

The days inched by until December12th when I had my X-ray. The radiographer agreed to do a general X-ray of the whole area including both hips, pubic symphysis and sacroiliac joint. The results were to be sent to my GP for me to discuss with him after Christmas.

By now I'd started to read up about Sacroiliac Joint Dysfunction and Pubic Symphysis Dysfunction or Symphysis Pubis Dysfunction (SPD) as it is more usually called, on the internet. I learned that I might be able to get a support belt or truss to help stabilise my pelvis. I ordered a sacroiliac joint belt, although I wasn't sure if it was exactly the right thing. I thought it had to be worth a try. After all I had now been in pain for six months. Other people clearly wore these things.

Was I supposed to manage my pelvic problems merely by pulling my tummy muscles in?

This belt was the first of many devices I was to buy over the internet to try to ease my pain. It was not the answer, not then anyway. I tried it out a few times over the next couple of months and always abandoned it quickly, as it seemed to make things worse.

On the 22nd of December we went to a Ramblers Christmas Party. It was now several months since I had rambled but I wanted to keep up the social side of the group. I spent virtually the whole evening talking about back pain. Everybody it seemed had a story to tell. Terry, the host, said he'd had a bad back for months and then he'd woken up one morning and it had miraculously gone. Well, bully for him. Tim recommended hanging upside down from the banisters. "Funny you should say that," I said. "My nephew, who also has back pain, has told me to hang from a door frame because it opens everything up." I wasn't ready to try either escapade yet. Tim also told me he could fix his own back "but don't ask me how I do it." This phrase was to echo round my head in the future as I dared to become bolder in what I tried. Someone else recommended something called a TENS unit. I'd never heard of this but apparently it was a device which gave you electronic stimulation through electrodes and was great for pain relief. It sounded really scary to an ignoramus like me but even so I decided to try one. I was sick of eating my own body-weight in pain-killers every day. After weeks of more pain I made my second internet purchase. The TENS unit arrived and was money well spent.

Christmas came and went and on the 30th December I

went back to my GP for the X-ray results. I didn't see the actual images; there was only a written report which the GP told me showed nothing – not even Symphysis Pubis Dysfunction. I later learned that this doesn't usually show on X-ray unless it is taken from a completely different angle – you have to stand on one leg like a stork for it. Well, if there was nothing to show how could I ask for an appointment with an orthopaedic consultant, and the GP didn't seem to want to offer one. Would he even still believe that I was in severe pain? Fortunately he did, believing that I might have a lot of inflammation in the painful areas. If I still didn't improve after further chiropractic he said he would refer me to the Pain Clinic at the hospital. I'd never heard of a Pain Clinic, but it sounded like a Good Thing, although I was still hoping to get better without having to go to hospital at all.

I went back to Meg in early 2006. She realigned the pubic symphysis and sacroiliac joints again on the 5th January and again on the 19th, at which point she told me she was going on holiday, but suggested I see her colleague Danielle, if I felt I needed further treatment. Danielle, she said, was very experienced and a second opinion might be valuable.

I was to meet Danielle sooner than planned. I woke in the small hours of January 25th in agony – somebody was trying to saw my pubic symphysis in half. I managed to get an emergency chiropractic appointment for that afternoon.

Danielle was young, intelligent, and had a warm smile and a lovely gentle manner. She was to play a big part in my story over the next few months. She was to say later that I was in quite a bad way when I arrived on that occasion. My pubic symphysis was "out", my right sacroiliac joint was locked and my piriformis muscle was very tight again. She treated me and advised me to come weekly again, which I did for a while.

January crept forward into February. Constant pain and lack of mobility – I could barely put one foot in front of another – made this dreary time of year even drearier. In desperation I bought a pain of crutches. My morale was at its lowest and I was frequently depressed.

It didn't help that my mother had begun to develop an obsession with "going home", although she wasn't unhappy where she was and was well cared-for. I was still visiting three times a week – I played cards and board games with her, read her light-hearted poems, bought videos for us to watch together and even played the piano for residents' sing-alongs, doing all I could to entertain her. Once I even moved her bed, which was not on castors – I needed to accommodate a small table and there was no-one else around – by lying flat on the floor and pushing it with my feet. When the weather improved later in the year we sat together in the conservatory, took short walks in the grounds and drank our tea and strolled round the enclosed courtyard garden, sheltered from any breezes. Other members of the extended family visited as often as they could and she probably had more visits than any other resident. We all cheered her up, but we couldn't get inside her head, where her memory and thoughts were getting more and more mixed up.

Apart from my visits to the care home I maintained my teaching – just, did my exercises and a few domestic chores and took short walks as prescribed. The rest of the time I lay flat on my back on the sofa applying ice, doing puzzles, reading, listening to music, or just lying there feeling sorry for myself.

Hours, days went by in this fashion. I wished I were back in London, I wished I'd never moved. What was the point of being surrounded by beautiful countryside when I couldn't enjoy it? Then I realised that being back in London wouldn't fix the problem. What I actually wanted was not to go back to London, but to go back to a time before the injury. Knowing that the clock couldn't be turned back did nothing to help my mood.

I looked forward to my chiropractic sessions like a junkie to his fix. I often felt improvement in the mornings, but the pain would worsen as the day wore on. My new TENS unit was coming into its own now. It made a considerable difference to pain relief during the day and then I knocked myself out with pain killers and amitriptyline at night.

After my third session with Danielle I recorded with joy the small victory that she had not needed to readjust my pubic symphysis that time – it had "held" for a whole week! I told her that Ed and I had planned a weekend in London but that I was dubious about going. "Do go," she said, "It'll do you good, so long as you're careful." I decided she was right – it was time to get off my sofa and give myself a change of scene.

It was indeed a lovely break. We stayed with friends and caught up with other old friends, and talked and shared good food and wine. On our last night, however, pain in my pubic symphysis woke me up. Ice – I needed ice. Danielle swore by it. I groped my way in the dark down to the kitchen, found ice in the freezer and started rummaging in drawers for a plastic bag to put it in. What the hell am I doing, I thought – what kind of a crazy life am I being forced to live, creeping round my friend's kitchen like a thief at 2am in the morning? Amazingly I didn't wake anyone up.

By the 22nd February Danielle was fixing my pubic symphysis again. She said I had an unusual injury. Perhaps it required unusual treatment? Maybe I should go to the hospital – to the obstetrics department! Symphysis pubis dysfunction was normally associated with pregnancy. She had adjusted it with a slightly different technique this time, which left me unable to sit down for about four hours and I did an afternoon's teaching and ate my supper standing up.

She also suggested I might try acupuncture. I knew nothing about it. But suddenly, by coincidence, it seemed to be everywhere, including on the telly and I kept meeting people who recommended it. So it seemed I had nothing to lose by trying it. Throughout March I had five sessions with Danielle's colleague, Alan, who put needles into different places trying different regimes. As a treatment it was not painful, but neither did I feel that it had helped. Alan suggested that I might have torn some tendons but I wasn't convinced. My pain went up and down and changed on a daily, even hourly basis.

My GP decided to refer me to the Pain Clinic, and also suggested I book an appointment directly with the hospital physiotherapy department about my SPD. I also asked him about booking an MRI scan. Friends had been urging me to have one and I'd now begun to think it would be a good idea. I was in total confusion – I'd been told I had a groin strain, I didn't have a groin strain, I had "referred" pain, I had symphysis pubis dysfunction, I had sacroiliac joint dysfunction, I might have torn some tendons, I might have sprained some ligaments (whatever they were), I should rest, I should exercise. In other words I was in a total muddle.

"I can't authorise a scan," my GP said, "You'll have to wait for your Pain Clinic appointment."

"What if I pay for it myself?"

"Oh, in that case I can do it. It'll come through quite quickly, probably next week."

"I don't understand the relationship between the NHS and private medicine," I said, at which he roared with laughter and said, "I'm not sure that I do either!"

On the 7th April I had my seventeenth chiropractic session and the last for some time. Danielle had to adjust my pubic symphysis again because the right side was anterior – sticking forwards. Between them she and Meg had now put it back "in" seven times, and the right sacroiliac joint many more times than that. Chiropractic clearly was not the answer for me. I even began to wonder if it was now doing more harm than good. Despite that I felt tremendously grateful to Meg and Danielle both of whom had tried so hard on my behalf.

As usual after my treatment I felt better for a day or two, then worse again. I hurt in all the usual places – pubic symphysis, sacroiliac joint, lower back, thigh muscles. I felt exhausted and worn out with pain.

My appointment with the hospital physio came through for 11th April, my MRI scan for the following day and the Pain Clinic referral was in the pipeline. With spring now here my spirits lifted a little, and with new practitioners and new investigations to come perhaps I could afford to hope a little. In a slightly better frame of mind I attended my first appointment with the hospital physio.

CHAPTER 3

The "Shopping List"

The Hospital and Functional Restoration Programme

I had prepared notes for the hospital physio, Sharon, but she wasn't very interested in them. She had a set routine to go through and she only wanted to tick her boxes. My heart sank as I was looking for someone who could think outside the box. She said she was not prepared to treat me if I was having "chiropractic" – she almost spat the word out. I said I'd stopped for the time being, though my hackles rose in defence of Meg and Danielle. I was also astonished. Although I was vaguely aware that it was considered "alternative" I had never expected such a reaction. She then said that there was not a shred of evidence that the heat machines and ultrasonic machines used by private physios had any effect whatsoever. My heart sank lower – this was not a good start.

If all these things didn't work, what did? Exercises she said. She examined me and made me lift my legs, bend, and stretch. She thought my pubic symphysis might be slightly out but seemed more interested in my back. It was very stiff, she said, and could be "referring" pain to my groin area. Oh this business of referred pain! It seemed a complete mystery to me. She gave me one new exercise only. I was to lean backwards, then pull myself slowly up to a normal stance. I now know this is a McKenzie back exercise with the rather cumbersome name of "Extension in Standing". I was to do ten of these every two hours, continue with pelvic floor exercises and come back and see her in a week.

The next appointment was in the obstetrics department – Danielle was right! What was I, clearly on the wrong side of fifty-five, doing here among the pregnant twenty or thirty-somethings? I felt most uncomfortable. Eventually Sharon arrived with Felicity, a specialist in the pelvis. At least that meant she was taking my pubic symphysis pain seriously. Neither of them had anything new to offer regarding it however, and Sharon's only message was to emphasise the importance of exercises. She said more or less the same thing at my third appointment a fortnight later; saying a global approach to get me moving would be a better way forward, rather than pushing in bits that might come out again. I didn't know there was another approach – if bits come out it had seemed to me they've got to be pushed in again, which is why I had persisted with chiropractic for so long. But she was right about getting me moving – I hadn't realised how tight and weak all my muscles had become from my lying around on the sofa all winter. Nobody had explained that my sedentary behaviour was actually compounding the problem. Sharon wanted to send me to a programme known as "Functional Restoration", which would give me targeted exercises and was very good, she said, for getting people moving again – people like me who had chronic pain.

Chronic pain! That was the first time anyone had used the expression and I didn't like it one bit. I agreed to go to the programme to see what they could offer. Meanwhile I had had my MRI scan and when the results came the report was negative. No cause could be found for my pain. No torn tendons or ligaments, no bursitis – nothing. At first I was tremendously disappointed. I spent hours poring over the images, trying to understand them, imagining I would find something that an experienced radiographer had missed! How could I be in so much pain and yet there be nothing to show for it? Then I began to feel relieved because I felt that with an X-ray and a scan behind me, both showing negative results, there was nothing really awful happening. Was there?

I hadn't really taken to Sharon but rather to my surprise I found her exercises seemed to help. I wondered later if pulling myself up from an extended back position activated deep abdominal muscles that pulled the pubic symphysis back in. Gradually it began to hurt less and my back began to loosen up. I felt cautiously optimistic, although I still had groin pain and thigh pain.

I had made myself practise the piano throughout the spring, wanting to do something slightly more challenging than Sudoku puzzles. In early May I played in the adult classes at the Cheltenham Performing Arts Festival. I arrived at the town hall bearing paraphernalia of lumbar rolls and cushions and I nipped into the Ladies every two hours to do my back extension exercises, much to the astonishment of several little girls in their ballet clothes also using the facilities. But if doing back exercises every two hours was going to get me better, then I would do back exercises every two hours no matter what.

The following day I started the Functional Restoration programme (FRP). I was to continue here for six weeks. I was given very gentle stretching exercises, which I was to build up gradually over time. It wasn't that I hadn't been doing exercises – everybody I'd seen had given me a different set. Always I tried and then abandoned them because they stirred up pain. Nonetheless I would try yet again as this was what I was on the programme for.

Despite constant pain in lots of areas there was no doubt that the pubic symphysis seemed to have settled down. I was very cautiously daring to hope that Danielle's last adjustment – now five weeks ago – and Sharon's back exercises had finally stabilised it. Of all the pains I had, none was quite as awful or as debilitating as that. How anybody copes with pregnancy or a new-born baby with this condition is beyond my imagining.

On May 15th I attended for my out-patient appointment at the Pain Clinic. I saw a consultant, Dr Davidson, who took my history, read the notes I'd made and a letter Danielle had written him – "a very sensible letter," he said – and gave me a thorough examination. He said my injury was similar to the sort of shearing injury a footballer might sustain – a sports injury. He then said I might have a problem with my hip. He suspected it might be inflamed – he called it "irritable hip" – which was something that would not have shown up on either the X-ray or the scan. He wanted to give me a cortisone injection to calm the irritability down.

Cortisone! I'd once had tennis elbow cured with cortisone and it had seemed to me to be a miracle cure at the time. Yes, I'd go along with this. Groin pain now seemed to be my dominant pain. I could never quite accept that it was "referring" from my back. *Please don't tell me I've got arthritis,* I thought. The big A. I had no intention of getting this until I was in my eighties like my mother. But I'd had an accident, hadn't I. A definite injury that had been the start of all my problems. No reason then to even think about arthritis.

"What about my sacroiliac joint?" I asked.

"We've got a shopping list," Dr Davidson said. "We'll start with your hip and then see where we go from there."

I mentioned another area of pain just in a bit from my groin, which Dr Davidson said could be caused by a trigger point. He could inject that as well and I could also have medical acupuncture. That might be next on our shopping list after cortisone injections. The final thing if nothing else worked would be to go to the Pain Management Clinic. I scarcely noticed this last remark. I was going to get better; I wasn't going to need Pain Management.

He looked at the MRI report and said I was quite unusual in having no findings at all. Often things show up which are not causing any pain and of which people are quite unaware! Even MRI scans don't show everything, he said – "there is no scan for pain." He spoke knowledgeably and quickly and said a lot of things that seemed to make sense but inevitably I forgot a lot of them by the time I got home. But one thing stuck. He kept turning to his colleague and talking about trigger points. What the hell were trigger points? And if I had them why had nobody told me about them before – after ten months of pain? I had already asked a lot of questions and my time was up. I was given a date a month away for the hip injection and sent on my way with instructions to keep on at the Functional Restoration programme because its exercises went hand in hand, he said, with his hip procedure.

As soon as I was home I went straight to Google to find out about trigger points. The simplest explanation seemed to be that they were small "knots" which formed in muscles when they'd been overloaded in some way. Well plenty of my muscles had been overloaded in the original injury and no doubt through walking awkwardly for the months following it. My head was buzzing with all that Dr Davidson had said and with this new information I was reading.

Meanwhile I had an exercise programme to attend. I went regularly – twice a week – and also did the exercises at home. Some were stretches; others were "circuit" exercises, the purpose of which was never clearly explained. My problem with the stretches, though, was that they seemed to make matters worse. And yet I was being told that I had to stretch, that stretching through the pain barrier would get my muscles working again. I continually tried, hoping the experts were right, but I began to have a love-hate relationship with stretches, as once again I stirred up pain in various places – usually in the groin, sometimes in the inner thigh, sometimes in the piriformis. Sometimes I felt as if my whole leg was wrongly fitted into my trunk. After one sleepless night I longed for the reassurance I got from Danielle. I booked an appointment with her, feeling guilty that the physios on the Functional Restoration programme and Dr Davidson wouldn't like it (he hadn't seemed too keen on chiropractors, despite the sensible letter) and then feeling angry that I was being made to feel guilty.

Danielle assured me that my body had not gone back to square one, which I was claiming it had – nothing like it. She told me she didn't want to see me till after the cortisone injection, which was due in two weeks' time and then only for a check-up. And even she said I should go to the Functional Restoration programme, so go I did.

But I began to be a bit canny. I carefully selected the exercises I felt able to do and left out the others. Some days I was able to walk quite well and I even climbed the seventy steps up Broadway Tower in the Cotswolds on Bank Holiday Monday, paying for it on the Tuesday, but only temporarily. I dared to take some risks as the injection was only a fortnight away now and I was pinning my hopes on it being a magical cure.

I was admitted to hospital for the morning of June 12th. In addition to Dr Davidson there was a radiographer – the procedure was done under X-ray – a nurse and a student in the theatre – quite a little party. Local anaesthetic went in first followed by the cortisone which I couldn't feel, but it was fascinating to watch it on the X-ray, curling round the ball of the hip.

"Well I think that's a pretty good hip movement," Dr Davidson said afterwards, as he grasped my leg and waggled it about in all directions. "Keep on with your exercises and increase your walking. I want you to walk. Climb over lots of stiles." Was that a wink?

He then decided to do two "trigger point" injections as well – one in the inner thigh where my muscles were very tight, and the other in my lower abdomen. I nearly shot through the roof on the second one – I felt as if I'd been knifed.

"I think you've scored a bull's-eye," said the nurse, adding gently to me, "Are you all right". Was I? I didn't know. I decided it would be a few days before I could say with certainty.

Six weeks later I was back in theatre for the second item on the shopping list – a cortisone injection into my right sacroiliac joint. This time it was done by Dr Davidson's senior registrar, under his guidance. She did an excellent job of it. "I might as well retire now," Dr Davidson said.

He wanted to inject the "trigger point" in my lower abdomen again, where the pain was no better, but I refused. I wasn't letting anyone near that area again with a needle. I told him that I'd read up about trigger points and was sure I had lots of them. He said the body couldn't take too many injections for them. Medical acupuncture would be a better bet, and I could have that in the autumn if I felt I still needed it then.

Over the summer I finished with the Functional Restoration programme, paced up my walking and monitored my progress. By the end of June some bits of me were definitely better. I could get in and out of the car and put my socks on much more easily. Hooray! My hip no longer "gave" on walking, something it had been inclined to do at most unexpected moments, completely unnerving me. Stretching, however, still remained a very variable activity. Some days the exercises made me feel looser, but on others I only had to overdo something the slightest bit to stir up pain for the rest of the day. It was a minefield that I hadn't learned to find my way through. One day when I had a particularly bad muscle spasm in my right thigh I started to use the heel wedge again. Result: an almost instant lessening of leg spasms. My right leg, I decided, might not be *actually* shorter (it had been measured three times by three different people) but it felt *functionally* shorter, though I had no idea why.

I more or less abandoned stretches and concentrated on walking. This was what I wanted to do; this was what was important to me. And at last I did feel some lessening of pain. For the first time in a year I found I could even enjoy life again. We were in the height of summer and the weather was glorious. The garden was looking good, thanks to Ed's work in it. We went to the Three Counties Show again and bought some garden furniture. We went to a sixtieth birthday party for the younger of my two brothers, turning the event into a weekend away.

July was even hotter. I had gradually paced up my walking after the hip injection from five minutes a day until I could walk almost a mile comfortably. Ed and I were back to the evening walks we so loved to do in the height of summer. On July 7th, a year and a day after the accident, I finally felt able to walk as far as the wobbly stile. I wanted to find out what kind of job had been made of mending it, and climb over it again and lay my ghosts.

No-one had mended it. We could not believe it. It's true we hadn't reported it, but walking was so popular in our area I felt confident somebody would have done. In the early days friends had suggested we sue the owner of the land for compensation. I had briefly considered it, but thought with dismay of the battle that would be bound to ensue, the costs, and the paperwork. It would be exhausting and draining and probably achieve nothing. I decided against it knowing I needed every ounce of my emotional reserves just to deal with the pain, just to survive and get through from one day to the next.

Now we reported it to everyone we could think of – the Ramblers, the local footpath committee, and the Public Rights of Way Office, enclosing photos of the damaged stile. Even then it wasn't mended until October, and not very satisfactorily at that. We couldn't help wondering how long it would take to work loose again.

The weather remained wonderful throughout July and as long as I was careful I continued to enjoy it. There was no doubt that I had come a long way from the wreck who'd lain all winter on the sofa. We went to open air theatre, and summer concerts, and took my mother to hear the band in the park. By the end of the month my walking was up to two miles. I was not without pain throughout all this time, but I was functioning so much better, which was giving me back a life. By now I'd even dared to come off most of my medication although I still used my TENS machine frequently and was grateful for it. "You can use it all day," Dr Davidson had said. We'd even dared to book a holiday – not too far away, in case I felt I couldn't cope and wanted to come home. We left for Devon on the last day of July, a week after my second cortisone injection.

I almost lost my new husband and even newer car on the second day of our holiday. Driving up a 1 in 3 hill from Babbacombe Bay near Torquay we were nearly mown down by a hulking great 4x4 which was bearing down on us, forcing us into the side. After that our car couldn't seem to get a purchase on the gritty steep slope.

"It might be better if you got out," said Ed. *Thanks. Do I really weigh that much?* He made two more attempts to get going, to no avail. Then he started to go backwards and I watched in horror as the car rolled seawards. But it was a deliberate ploy to reach a slightly less steep part of the road. With a squeal of brakes and smoke coming from the tyres he suddenly shot forwards in first gear and went racing up the hill. I followed on foot to find him in a parking bay, letting the engine cool. I suddenly realised that was the first hill I'd walked up since the injury – and I felt fine!

That was quite enough excitement for one holiday and nothing as dramatic happened after that. We drove on to Cornwall and settled into our hotel near Fowey for four days.

The following day, armed with walking poles, we set out on a coast path walk, intending to do a mile or two and then go back. But, every time I stopped for a break, I wanted to go on. The day was so clear, the views over the estuary so beautiful and somehow the more I walked the better I felt. We ended up doing over five miles, then sat for hours overlooking the open sea, had a cream tea in the little village we'd reached, then went back to our hotel by boat. It was a day I was to remember with a mix of joy and nostalgia for years to come.

It was the same most days – the more I walked the better I felt. The coast path goes up and down much more steeply than one imagines, but Danielle had taught me how to brace myself to go upstairs and I used the same technique now, to get me up the hills. We walked on the coast path, walked all round Heligan Gardens, walked around St. Mawes, then went to North Devon and walked at Bideford, Appledore, Westward Ho! and Hartland Point. We also me up with family at Castle Drogo and walked around the grounds there. Walking was great. I had conquered walking!

But I was finding it harder and harder to get comfortable sitting. Normal sitting on a chair was bad enough, but sitting on the sands on the one and only day we spent on the beach seemed virtually impossible. While Ed went swimming in the sea, I squirmed around on the ground trying and failing to get comfortable. If I sat with my legs straight out in front of me I just felt so tight in my thighs and in my groin that I couldn't stand it. Eventually I found a modicum of comfort from assuming a more or less prone position. This felt like the same problem I got from stretching, only now I was getting it from normal activity and I couldn't understand it at all, but clearly something wasn't right. Dr Davidson had laid great emphasis on trigger points. I could only assume it was these which were keeping my leg muscles tight.

I rang the hospital to update them on how I felt after my SIJ injection as I'd been instructed to do, and was told I'd hear from them again after I described these latest problems.

Acupuncture was the next thing Dr Davidson had mentioned – medical acupuncture, which is different from traditional Chinese acupuncture. Would this finally sort me out?

CHAPTER 4

A Knotty Problem

Trigger Points and Acupuncture

Before leaving for holiday I had ordered a book called "The Trigger Point Therapy Workbook", by Clair Davies, an American massage therapist. It had five stars and rave reviews on Amazon and so I decided I had to have it. It was waiting for me on my return from holiday. I began to read it avidly. And I read the following sentence and wanted to write it in huge letters and frame it. The author had suffered with a very painful shoulder that no one seemed able to fix. He wrote *"Variations on the theme of exercise and stretch were all I heard, despite my protests that stretching made my pain worse, not better"*. At last! Hadn't I been saying for months that stretching made me worse? I was not alone!

So what are trigger points? They are small contraction knots in muscle tissue, which come about when a muscle has been overtaxed in some way. They can affect a muscle by keeping it both tight and weak. And they can *refer* pain to other sites. Part of the mystery of "referred" pain started to unravel. The gurus of trigger points are two highly respected American doctors, Janet Travell and David Simons (Janet Travell was appointed personal physician to President

Kennedy in 1961), whose seminal work "Myofascial Pain and Dysfunction: The Trigger Point Manual" first published in 1983, is the Bible of trigger points. It is extremely expensive and probably very difficult for a lay person to understand. The book I had bought was a sort of Trigger Point Guide for Dummies. It was easy to read, was a mine of information and also told me, most importantly, how to locate and treat trigger points with self-massage.

I'd never poked at my muscles before – who does? But now I began a systematic palpation of every inch of my tight legs. Was all this tightness due to trigger points? If muscles are used wrongly for a long time cascades of trigger points could develop, the book said. Even more enlightening was this sentence: *"An apparent short leg is sometimes simply a collection of long-standing trigger points drawing up that side of the body."* Was this the explanation for my functionally shorter right leg?

I began to massage my "knots" the way the book said with all the zeal of a religious convert. I should massage them between six and twelve times per day, the book said, up to point seven on the pain scale. Well that's pretty high, and it was painful to do but I tried it anyway.

Within days I was covered in bruises. This was not a good start. Gradually, over many months, I learned to refine the technique and realised that I could get good results from far less pressure and that massaging two or three times a day was enough. Eventually I bought a rubber ball, as recommended, and learned to massage my bum with it against the bathroom wall. It was very effective and I kept a second ball in my handbag and would sometimes nip into a loo almost anywhere and give my bum a quick ball-massage to give my tight piriformis almost instant relief!

In those early days I was making plenty of mistakes and got fed up with my cack-handed self-treatment. I was pleased when I was sent an outpatient appointment with the hospital acupuncturist, Mr Lindsey, for early September.

Mr Lindsey assessed me, moving my hip through all its planes whilst feeling for trigger points. He said I had what the Americans would describe as a "disordered hip". He wrote a list for me of the five muscles that he would needle, which included my friend the piriformis (in the bum), the adductor longis (the inner thigh) and the iliopsoas – consisting of the psoas and iliacus muscles. This is one of what is called the "hip flexors" and it joins the top of your thigh to your lumbar vertebrae. I was to become particularly well acquainted with this one as, when tight, it can cause a multitude of problems.

I felt things were going very well and took a liking to this rather serious, but very thorough man, until he said he wanted me to stretch my psoas. But it was stretching that caused all my problems! Didn't he know it was trigger points that *prevented* me from stretching? I said I couldn't stretch, that I'd done every stretching exercise under the sun, but he said "you've not done this one" and indeed I hadn't. It was a lunge. I did it there and then under his direction and said, "it's not now it hurts, it'll be in an hour's time." Which it did.

His first available appointment for treatment was September 29th. As it was now only the 4th, that was nearly a month away. I wondered how I would get through the next four weeks as my body seemed to get tighter by the day.

By September 8th I had stirred up a lot of pain from doing

the lunge. I had pain in the pubic symphysis – a place which hadn't bothered me for months – pain in the groin and a trapped nerve giving me sciatic-type pains all down the inside of my leg. The next day the pain moved to my back. By 20th I could scarcely walk again. It was depressing. I'd been so much better in August – I'd even gone on a five-mile ramble at the end of the month. Surely I wasn't going to go backwards again?

Finally the 29th came. Mr Lindsey asked me straight away whether I'd done the lunge stretch, and I told him about the trouble it had caused. Before I knew it he'd stuck a needle once into the psoas, twice into my back, stretched my leg and told me that was it for today. The needles had gone in and out – I hadn't sat there for fifteen minutes with a dozen sticking out of me like a hedgehog, as I'd done with Alan six months previously.

Seeing my bruises Mr Lindsey asked me if I was looking for "knots" and when I said yes, he told me to stop massaging myself. I did – for a while.

Although I had hoped for improvement I had another bad week with pains shunting round between the usual places and now moving up to my neck and shoulders. Whatever was going on? I was using my TENS unit for hours at a time and was back on sleeping pills. But I did feel some improvement after the second treatment and more so after the third one in mid-October. Mr Lindsey was working round the muscle groups in an order. He was, he said, "unravelling the history" and was pleased that my body was responding so well.

I left after that session feeling more hopeful than I had for ages. I had two more appointments booked, the next of which was three weeks away, as Mr Lindsey was going on holiday. So I thought I'd try to address some of the neck and shoulder pain that had crept on recently – I knew not why. I remembered the one massage I'd had with Kim a year ago and how my muscles had felt considerably looser afterwards. With my trigger point manual praising the benefits of massage I decided it was time to take it more seriously as a treatment.

Kim had left the Natural Health Centre and been replaced by Nadine who was young and friendly. I had two massages from her in October. She said the muscles in my shoulders and neck were like rocks, and she also found plenty of "knots" throughout the length of my back. In fact she found aches and pains in places I never knew I had! I began to understand that, through walking awkwardly as I had been doing for months, my whole muscular system had got out of kilter and tension had been created everywhere. After her treatments I would ache all over, but I did feel a lot looser – surprisingly so.

If massage was as beneficial as I was finding, were there other treatments which might help? I returned to my "Complete Family Health" with its section on complementary medicine. One thing that sounded interesting was Rolfing. It aimed to free up knots and adhesions that form in the connective tissue surrounding muscles, returning the muscles to their proper elasticity. I looked it up on the internet and read a whole lot more, which seemed to indicate that it would be really appropriate for me. It would be a whole body treatment, integrating the entire system. That sounded just what I wanted because I felt that my whole body was somehow "wrong", and though I liked both Mr Lindsey and Nadine I felt their treatments were addressing "bits" of me. The tightness now seemed to go from my neck to my knees. It sounded crazy, but I could only describe it as having something like a second skin under my first one, which was glued onto all the muscles below so that unless I stayed perfectly still I had pain whichever way I moved. My whole body didn't seem to fit any more.

I had a few good days – perhaps because the massage was taking effect, perhaps because I did less. I was hopeful when I saw Mr Lindsey again in early November, but my optimism was to prove unfounded. Another bad week followed and I went to what should have been my fifth acupuncture session in a far less happy mood. Even so I was unprepared for the bombshell that was about to happen.

"I don't think this treatment is doing you any good," Mr Lindsey said. "I think we should stop it. I'm going to refer you back to Dr Davidson who can recommend you for Pain Management."

I was stunned. Totally gobsmacked. I hadn't been in a car crash, or had a ski-ing accident or fallen out of a tree. I'd had what seemed the most trivial of falls and sixteen months later I was being labelled an invalid for life.

"You mean there's no help for me."

"I didn't say that. Pain Management…"

"Oh pain management," I retorted rudely (I'm sorry to say.) "You're saying I can't be helped, I've just got to live with it."

"I didn't say that. They can do a lot to help you at Pain Management – God, if you knew how many times I've had this conversation. They really can help."

I was reeling with shock, and to my annoyance starting to

cry. As I pulled myself together my mind began to race. Clearly the NHS was running out of options for me but I was determined to get better. "All right," I said. "I'll go to Pain Management. But while I'm waiting *(it might be weeks or months away)* I want to try something else. I'd been thinking about Rolfing."

"Rolfing!" He nearly fell off his chair. "Do you know what Rolfing is? I've had Rolfing and it's the most painful thing I've ever experienced. I can't see how it would help your problem."

Later when I'd had time to think it over I was to realise that this statement begged a lot of questions. What was my problem? Did he know what it was? If so, why didn't he tell me? And if he didn't, how was he to know whether Rolfing would or wouldn't help it?

For now I said, "What can you suggest then?" As an acupuncturist surely this man had knowledge of other complementary therapies. I had a fifteen-minute slot with him and I was going to milk every second of it. I believed him to be a kind man who wanted to help – I remembered the patience with which he'd explained things in my initial outpatient appointment. He reached for his notepad and wrote a list, which included Bowen Therapy – which I'd never heard of – Tai Chi, Alexander Technique and Pilates.

I left his clinic for the last time clutching this list, and went to meet Ed who was waiting in the car. We were going to spend the weekend with our London friends. I told him all that had just happened as we ate our sandwiches. He took it all in quietly. I was still numb with shock as we set off on our journey.

"How's the acupuncture going?" was my friend's first

question on our arrival and I had to tell her the morning's events. She seemed as shocked as I had been. It was great to have sympathetic listeners to talk over my problems with and to be spoilt – she and her husband were, as always, very generous hosts. And this time I didn't have to creep down in the small hours and pinch their ice!

Among other things I told them I'd started having massage and my friend said she knew someone with a hectic lifestyle – "the only person I know who hoovers her house every day" – who had a hot stone massage once a month to de-stress. A hot stone massage! That sounded fantastic! Clearly I had a lot to learn about complementary therapies. This was the moment at which I decided to pursue a quest – to put serious money in until I got answers. I didn't have a mortgage, my children were grown-up and off my hands and I didn't lead an extravagant lifestyle – I couldn't even if I wanted to. So I had a certain amount of disposable income. What more important way to spend it?

To be fair, I'd had a reasonable amount of NHS time, if I totted up the physio with Sharon, the Functional Restoration programme, the outpatient appointments, the cortisone injections and five acupuncture appointments, the last having been the aborted one. Of course there was a limit to what they could give me. I knew the good old NHS would look after me if I ever got something ghastly like cancer, but I didn't think that would be likely for years, if at all.

But saying "we can't help you anymore" – as Dr Davidson did in the letter I received late in November – is not the same as saying "You can't be helped." And he did offer me Pain Management in the same letter – I knew I shouldn't dismiss it.

Pain Management, though, didn't sound like answers. I wanted answers. Even if I had to live with pain for the rest of my life I wanted to know *why*. Nobody had yet got to the bottom of things. For the next few nights I lay awake, feeling sore over my whole body. Surely I didn't have to put up with this for the rest of my life? Surely something could be done? I realised that, no matter how accurately I tried to describe my problems, nobody else could get inside my body and experience what I was feeling. I had to follow my instincts and react to what my body was telling me. Initially I decided to carry on my own self-treatment of trigger points and to book Nadine for more massage. I would also do more internet research and see what came up. And there was Mr Lindsey's list and also Rolfing, which I was still considering, despite his reaction to it. The NHS might have finished its shopping – I was just about to start mine.

I had a plan now. And with a plan comes hope. I didn't know then that there were many more setbacks to come and that it would be another two and a half years before I got the answers I craved.

CHAPTER 5

Under my Skin

Massage and Rolfing

What, I asked Nadine, as she kneaded and pummelled the muscles of my back and shoulders, did she know about Bowen Therapy or Rolfing? Not a lot about Bowen, although she'd heard good reports of it, but she actually knew and worked with a Rolfer in Cheltenham, who she said was lovely and she could thoroughly recommend.

"Who goes to Rolfing?" I asked mindful of the comment that it "wouldn't help your problem."

"People like you."

Meanwhile I was having such trouble again with my pelvis, back and leg that I realised there was only one place to go – back to Danielle. She had been my rock for the first part of the year and I needed a rock again. This was my first visit to her for four months. Her adjustments included realigning my pubic symphysis, which depressed me, because when it had stabilised the previous April I thought that was it. Done, sorted. Clearly it wasn't. Then I remembered that it had felt dodgy – although I had tried to deny it – ever since a ramble in early September, where there had been a lot of hill climbing. Neither the pubic symphysis nor the sacroiliac joint likes hills if either is at all weak, I was to discover – repeatedly – in my efforts to climb some in the coming months. If either of those joints is weak, hill walking will really make it complain. Walking with Ed in Cornwall had been fine, probably because – I was later to realise – of the effectiveness of the cortisone at that time. Also we could go at my pace, but rambling required keeping up with the party and it was clear that I couldn't do that. Rambling was put on the back burner for many months.

It was now December and I didn't feel like doing anything very much but thought it might be worth trying the "gentle" Bowen technique. It had been top of Mr Lindsey's list after all. It didn't seem to do anything for me though, so I called a halt after two sessions and battened down the hatches for another Christmas. It was depressing. I was still in a lot of pain and felt that, after such an improved summer I was back to square one, and at the worst time of the year.

I would pursue Rolfing, I decided – the more I read about it on the internet, the more my instincts said it was the right treatment for me. I felt mummified, as if my whole muscular system was in a straitjacket and this treatment promised to release the tight tissues of my whole body.

However, in January – we were now into 2007 – I got side-tracked after a chance meeting with two Chinese doctors. I went to a private musical recital, hoping to network with some other musicians, as I still knew no other musical people in the area. It was a Sunday afternoon, and I was so tight I could barely sit down, which soon became evident to the whole audience. In the interval I was introduced to Dr Zhang with the comment "he helps problems like yours". Dr Zhang gave me a few surreptitious pokes finding the exact places that hurt. He told me his wife Cindy could easily cure me with Chinese massage, a deep foot massage – this was meat and drink to them. Easily cured! I took Cindy's phone number and went home to tell Ed, wondering what on earth he'd think.

"Shall I try it?" I asked him. He didn't see why not. And I thought – foot massage? Sounds fine. Bone crunching – been there – fine. Needles – done that – not a problem. Being walked on – what the hell – I'll try anything now.

I rang Cindy in the morning and she offered me an appointment for the same afternoon. At first I wondered what I was doing, as I waited in what looked like the front of a Chinese takeaway, at the interesting end of the High Street but thought I'd better go through with it. When Cindy was ready she took a brief history then took me through to a room at the back where I lay down, fully clothed on a mattress on the floor. Then she started the foot massage. For half an hour she massaged my gluteals and my hips. They were like rocks, she said. Now where had I heard that before?

The massage was deep – boy, was it deep! It was painful! My back hurt, my hips hurt, all my bum muscles hurt, on both sides. I ached for two days afterwards. Yet it was a good deep pain and felt as if it might do some good. I was also given acupuncture into my back and sent home with a packet of pills made from herbs – the complete Chinese medical approach she said. I was to cut down on meat and eat no fish while I was taking them. What the hell was in these pills? I had no idea – the writing on the packet was all in Chinese!

In the end I had seven treatments. And sometimes I felt better and sometimes I felt worse and although Cindy did loosen me up quite a bit for a while, none of the treatments seemed to last. One day I suddenly realised that, to get in even deeper, she was standing on me – and she was no lightweight! I nearly died of shock – it was only five weeks since Danielle had realigned my pubic symphysis! Then she put the acupuncture needles in and one of them sent an electric shock right down to my right foot. "The sciatic nerve", she said – "Do you good." Afterwards I felt better, indeed it was the first time I'd actually felt better immediately on getting up from the couch. But it was all a bit dramatic and for the last two sessions I asked her not to repeat anything so drastic.

By the last session there was no doubt that my left "good" side was much looser and freer, but the right was still tight and I still had spasms that came and went as well as the ever present backache. Cindy found that my right sacroiliac joint was out – what a surprise. By this time I had agreed to call it a day anyway and had already booked Danielle for another chiropractic session. She would put my SIJ in, I knew. Cindy agreed it was time to stop her treatment, that it hadn't been as effective as she'd hoped.

"Have you had many failures?" I asked her.

"Only two," she replied downheartedly, "One very elderly lady – and now you."

Not very comforting. It seemed I just was a real bugger to fix.

I had seen Danielle a couple of times over the winter and now I went back to have myself realigned yet again. It would be my last treatment with her for a long time. She was due to go on maternity leave in a week or two. She had been talking for a while about my going to see a physiotherapist who specialised in hips, as she thought there might still be a problem there, and she said she would do some investigating to find me a suitable person. I felt touched by her concern and willingness to help. Months later I was to understand that she was trying to get to the underlying cause of my *mechanical* problems. By now though, I was feeling so tight throughout my whole body that having my *muscular system* treated was the only thing I could concentrate on, and I don't think I'd really understood at this point that muscles don't usually tighten unless there is some underlying mechanical cause. In any case wasn't Dr Davidson supposed to have fixed my hip with his magic cortisone injection? My hip at that time was one of the few places that didn't hurt.

I bought and read another book, this time about sciatica and piriformis syndrome, and then another about backs – by now I had acquired a small library. "Treat your Own Back" by Robin McKenzie demonstrated the McKenzie method, which was widely established and I recognised one of the exercises as the one that Sharon had given me nearly a year ago. That had made me feel better and trying the exercises now I did indeed feel better – for a while. But as with everything else improvement didn't last and I abandoned them for about a year.

Instead I continued with self-massage. There was no doubt I could get some relief, if temporarily, from this process. Done gently, the massage, along with a few very gentle stretches, did help to make the pain and tightness more manageable. But usually I massaged too hard with a "no pain no gain" mentality, resulting in bruising. Let's face it; I didn't really know what I was doing. I wanted some more professional help. And this time I wasn't going to get side-tracked. This time I was going for Rolfing.

Rolfing was a turning point. It was to free me from constant muscular pain and tightness more than anything else I'd had to date. So it did "help" my problem. I arrived for my first appointment barely able to walk in March, and finished in October – it was a drawn-out procedure for a number of reasons – and went walking in the Black Mountains. Even so it was not by itself to be the Holy Grail and it was to be the end of that year – 2007 – before I began to understand some of the reasons why my problems kept coming back.

It was no picnic. Web-sites that say it is "uncomfortable" are understating the problem – it is painful. Mr Lindsey was right in that. But I was in pain all the time anyway, and I took the view that I could endure a bit more if it led to long-term gain. Women, after all, are used to pain – we have it once a month from the age of about twelve and massively bigger dollops of it when we have babies.

Charlotte, the Rolfer recommended by Nadine, had a lovely open, warm personality and I took to her straight away. It didn't take her long to discover that I was very tight everywhere from head to toe. My body was "locked up", she said. But this time I could feel the treatments doing me good right from the start and I knew I was going to stick the full course of ten sessions. I knew it was not a quick fix, but I literally felt my taut body unwind session by session. Moreover, Rolfing claims that the changes it makes in the body are permanent. I was full of hope. The Pain Management programme, I now heard, was due to start in May. Maybe I'd be pain free by then and wouldn't need to go!

Rolfing originated from the work of the American Dr Ida Rolf, who always referred to her methods as "Structural

Integration", but the nickname "Rolfing" was adopted in California in the late 1960s and it stuck. The treatment works on the connective tissue, or fascia, that surrounds every muscle of our body – hence the word myofascial, which is to do with muscles and fascia. In other words I did have a "second skin" – we all do. You can see it best in a chicken breast before it is cooked. Between the skin and the flesh (muscles) is a thin membrane. This is the fascia, and it is this that can get distorted and tight. My feeling that my body no longer "fitted" was not inaccurate – my whole fascial system was out of alignment. Tight fascia can also "lock in" trigger points. When the fascia is lengthened and freed the muscles have room to work properly and trigger points can often be resolved.

Charlotte said it was helpful to imagine your body as an old-fashioned tent with the skeleton being the tent poles and the muscles and fascia the canvas. If your tent falls over you need to put the poles *and* the canvas back in position. If your body becomes misaligned through injury or poor posture, putting the bones back in position with treatments such as chiropractic, may not be enough if tight muscles and fascia are constantly pulling them out of balance again. Rolfing aims to realign the "canvas" so that the whole system is better balanced.

The work involves deep pressure into the tissues, with the practitioner's hands then moving very slowly upwards whilst the pressure is maintained. Unlike massage no oils are used. It is slow – half an hour can be spent on one leg. But by this process the fascia is actually moved and stretched under the skin, and muscular tension is released. After each session I felt lighter and freer in my body in ways I would not have thought possible.

Quite separately from Charlotte's work I noticed rather worryingly that my hip was going "clonk" again, something which had stopped after the cortisone injection. Was Danielle right after all, to say I had a hip problem? One day when my whole hip and pelvis felt unstable I found an exercise on the internet where I sort of pulled the hip inwards. It seemed to cure the clonking, and firm everything up – and I mean everything – hip, pubic symphysis and sacroiliac joint. For a few blissful moments I was pain free. I looked up more to do with hips and pelvic injuries and found a total minefield. It was more than I could cope with. And the following day I had so much pain I decided I shouldn't be messing about with things I didn't really understand. I had a depressing day. It was the start of my Easter holidays and I felt I should be striding up hills, instead of lying flat on the floor clutching myself in unmentionable places.

My fourth Rolfing session was very painful, but also very productive. Charlotte worked both legs from the tips of my toes right up to my pelvis. Had I ever sprained my right ankle she wanted to know? Yes I had. It was thirty years ago but she could tell, after all this time! Your body holds old patterns of scar tissue forever it seems, until worked on in this way. She said it was like rubber there, and she worked hard to free it. All the way up my shin was tight, right up to my knee. Then working up my thigh – the thigh which had given me so much trouble for months – she found the adductors and the hamstrings were stuck together, and at the top in a place I'd known was painful for months she freed what she said felt like a piece of gristle. By now I was exhausted and had to ask her to stop. But it had done the trick. That leg was freed up for a very long time. Now I could stretch it. Now I could lunge. Oh Mr Lindsey if only you could have seen me!

But it got worse before it got better. I had a flare-up after this for the next few days. It wasn't surprising when I think what had been done to me. It was my birthday and I took to my bed with bags of ice, saying I wanted nothing to do with birthdays or life in general. Maybe I should give up Rolfing – there was no doubt it was a painful procedure. But the following day I got up and did some gentle ball massage with amazing results. It seemed to free up some muscle spasm so that I was virtually pain free for a while. I was even able to garden! A rubber ball could help me more than any medicine, it seemed. When in doubt I needed to remember this. And I *would* stick with Rolfing. It made me feel so great over all. Life seemed particularly crazy at this time – one day feeling a wreck, the next, almost normal. Clearly some of the pain was due to muscle spasms which when released made me feel wonderful. Why the spasms kept coming back though, remained a mystery – a mystery I was still several months away from solving.

Charlotte went away after my first four sessions to do an Advanced Rolfing Course in Hawaii – lucky woman! – but I was to resume treatment with her in the autumn and in the spring of 2008. In some ways these later sessions I had with her were the most beneficial of all, perhaps because of the groundwork done in the early sessions. Meanwhile she handed me over to her daughter, Rachel, also a trained Rolfer as well as a Sports Massage Therapist.

Rachel turned out to be as delightful as her mother and gave me four further sessions in which she worked mainly on my psoas muscles – the ones that join the thigh to the lower back – and my hips, bum and thighs. I felt looser and freer everywhere afterwards and for a while pain-free again. For the next few days I added in pelvic tilts to my daily regime of exercises, simply for the joy of being able to move my pelvis up and down without pain. And at last the trigger point that Dr Davidson had so painfully injected was gone – hooray!

I sent a message via Nadine to Danielle asking about the hip physio she'd hoped to find for me, bearing in mind the recent hip concerns I'd had. A few days later Danielle's receptionist rang with the name and phone number of the physio – as well as the lovely news that Danielle had had a baby girl. I put off going to this physio for various reasons – mainly my involvement with Rolfing – and the longer I put it off, the more life intervened and other things happened. I often wonder now, how different things might have turned out if I'd gone then, but I didn't so it's useless to speculate.

Rachel gave me more exercises, recommended yoga and demonstrated MBT shoes – special trainers that have been designed to ensure you use your muscles correctly when walking and are supposed to help with back problems. I bought a pair at vast expense, but they always rubbed my heels so I never really got on with them. She even gave me some vouchers for a free hot stone massage, which I was unfortunately not able to redeem before they ran out. She was clearly trying to help me in every way she could. I was very grateful, and there was no doubt that I had improved considerably since first starting Rolfing in March, but I was also nowhere near to being pain free or "normal." Maybe I really was beyond help. In any case Rolfing, and all other treatments, now had to be put on hold, because at last the Pain Management programme was due to start. I was going to learn to Live With It.

CHAPTER 6

Grin and Bear it

Pain Management

Pain Management does exactly what it says on the tin. It does not set out to cure pain, but aims to give you coping mechanisms to manage a pain-filled life better. Over the next eight weeks I was to learn many techniques for managing pain and reducing its impact on my life – exercises, relaxation, distraction strategies, positive thinking, managing flare-ups, communication skills, setting targets and – perhaps the most important – pacing. It was thought-provoking and beneficial and in the end I felt very grateful that I'd had the chance to do it.

It had started with an introductory talk in February, to which Ed had come along with me, supportive as ever. This basically outlined what the programme would offer, at the end of which I signed up for a personal assessment to take place in the middle of March. After that I would get slotted into the next available programme. It seemed a long drawn-out process and I was very glad that I was pursuing my other treatments until then.

The personal assessment, when it came, consisted of a session with a physiotherapist followed by one with a psychologist. I described to the physio the treatments I'd had to date, including, at that stage, the first Rolfing session. Unsurprisingly she'd never heard of Rolfing – I had learned that it was not at all widely known. I remember promising to stop it if I hadn't completed the ten sessions by the time my Pain Management programme started. Obviously doing any alternative therapy at the same time would muddy the waters somewhat.

The session with the psychologist, Paula, was much more memorable. Something about her demeanour or her opening remarks had me, scarcely before I knew it, pouring out all my disappointments and problems to her. When I told her how we'd spent two years searching for our perfect retirement location, that we'd moved here specially to walk and garden and now I could do neither, she said "That's some dream to give up." I felt her compassion and empathy and wanted to howl.

I started telling her about the demands of my mother in her home and how I fielded her frequent, usually garbled, telephone calls, which often interrupted my teaching, my meals or even my sleep. I also told her that I visited three times a week. I was well aware that all of this was exacerbating my stress levels, which I'm sure wasn't helping my pain. Paula thought three visits a week was rather a lot and wondered whether I was doing it for her or for me. *To assuage my guilt, at having dumped her in a home – yes, I know, I know…* She suggested I cut down the visits.

"I have to go," I said, "She had a fall last week."

"But she didn't have a fall this week," she countered and indeed it was true that my mother had not only survived this latest fall unscathed, but had forgotten that she'd had it. "Care for the elderly," said Paula "is a marathon, not a sprint."

She then talked about the emotional journey it's necessary to go through from looking desperately for cures to acceptance of pain as a chronic condition. I guess it's a form of grieving, which everybody goes through and I knew I still hadn't quite got there and that I was still hoping for magic answers from Rolfing. After all if Rolfing cured me I needn't go to the Programme. I could ring up and cancel it, and let someone needier have the place. This was how I'd been thinking up till now. But there was a bit of me that began to open the door a chink to realise that Paula might be right and that I would have to accept that I had a chronic condition.

I drove home feeling as if a ton weight had been temporarily lifted from my shoulders. For a while I had unburdened myself to a sympathetic and professional listener, and the relief that gave me really did reduce my pain levels for the rest of the day. What's more I felt I had been given "permission" to cut down my visits to my mother, which I did – from three to two a week – and I don't think she noticed at all.

Six weeks later I started the programme proper. By this time I had had eight Rolfing sessions, but had not achieved my goal of being pain free. So off I went to the course. It was to be twelve sessions in all, twice a week for the first month, then once a week for the next month. Mindful of my GP's comment, "You get out of it what you put into it," I went along with what I hoped was an open mind.

In the first session we met the group leaders and our fellow sufferers. There were originally ten participants, although this quickly reduced to seven as two caught flu and one obviously changed her mind altogether as she disappeared without trace.

There were four members of staff – a psychologist, a physiotherapist, an occupational therapist and a nurse. Four members of staff to seven patients, twelve sessions each of two hours – a lot of resources were going into this.

We started by saying our names and describing our pain. Back pain was common. Two people had fibromyalgia – a painful muscular condition. Two had neuropathic pain – damaged nerves. What did I have? I was the only one who couldn't say. Yes, I had back pain, but also so much muscle pain, which moved around from day to day, even hour to hour. It was this lack of diagnosis and consequent lack of understanding on my part that really bugged me. Because of it I felt frustrated, frightened and fragile.

We were given folders containing masses of hand-outs, one of which was a goal sheet. I couldn't remember having any "goals" and was quite surprised to find that as a result of my individual assessment Paula had written down "acceptance and understanding of pain," "learning to relax," "positive thinking" and "pacing." Later I added others, but apart from "walking further" I tried to address those targets chosen for me in the first few weeks.

After coffee we had a session on stress. We were asked what some of the causes of stress were and someone shouted out "other people!" The group, which up till now had been quiet, with everyone feeling shy and no-one wanting to stand out, exploded. "And their silly questions," added another person. "What's the matter with you? You look all right." Another enthusiastic chorus of approval. Yes, how do you describe chronic pain to "normal" people, when there's nothing to show for it?

We learned about the stress or "fight or flight" response and about rabbits freezing in car headlights, and how we can stop it by learning relaxation techniques. And so we all began to practise "diaphragmatic breathing" – something that it is easier to do than to say. I went home with my head spinning from information overload.

Session two addressed "Pacing" with a capital "P" because of its significance in the programme. It really is one of the most important aspects of managing pain. People with chronic pain tend to have good and bad days. On their good days they try to cram everything in because it makes them feel "normal," we were told. Yes. Yes! *Yes*! **Yes**! It's so hard to accept that you're not normal, that you can't do what you used to. But then you get into what's known as "activity cycling." On a good day you overdo things, it stirs up pain which makes you feel worse, so you do less the next. Then, when you feel better you go headlong at things, overdo it, stir up pain again, so you feel worse again and do less. This can go on and on, in a downward spiral until you're doing practically nothing and end up in a deep depression. If, however, you do the opposite – if you start gently and pace everything on a daily basis with a rest or change of activity in between, you can build up to higher levels and achieve almost as much in the long run, but without the peaks and troughs. You could improve considerably, although at some point you would reach a plateau, where you would have to accept your limitations.

It sounds so obvious, but yet we don't do it. Over the course of the programme I learned to pace everything, from doing all household tasks and going shopping to more pleasurable things like going for my daily walk and doing the garden, both of which I paced initially in five to ten minute chunks. When you have to write it down and monitor everything you do on a daily basis and report back there's no room for cheating. With the course providers asking for your progress – positive and negative – every session, you couldn't get out of it. It was dinned into us, so that gradually after a few weeks it became a way of life. It had its advantages, I discovered. If my pain was stirred up after five minutes of hoovering I now had the perfect excuse for lying down and doing Sudoku guilt free.

Next addressed was "Goal Setting." At the end of every week we set ourselves targets – paced of course – and a week later we reported back on our success or lack of it. Since walking was my passion this had to be my number one goal. Rolfing had given my body sufficient improvements to enable me to start short walks in the spring, building up from the zero to which I had sunk back over the winter. I now set my target for half an hour, but with pacing in mind, built in a rest after fifteen minutes. I couldn't believe the difference it made. I slowly paced up my walking throughout June and early July, gradually adding in gentle hills and even stiles. Although at the moment it seemed to do nothing but rain, I was confident that when the summer holidays and good weather came I would be able to walk well.

We learned more relaxation techniques and were given CDs to take home and use on a daily basis. You could relax to music, or you could follow a storyline on the CD or – my preferred technique – you could "visualise" some really nice place as you let your muscles go, one by one. Memories of sitting on the Cornish cliffs above the beautiful Fowey estuary the previous year came flooding back to me when I tried it. In spite of this I never really got good at relaxation as a technique. "Emptying my mind," as you were asked to do was scary – I might never be able to fill it again! And "visualising" Cornwall soon made me depressed that I couldn't be there walking the coast path – that I might never walk the coast path again. Having nothing to occupy my brain with made me concentrate on the pain more. If on the other hand I used my relaxation sessions to do Sudoku, solve crosswords or read books, I felt I was spending the time usefully. I was relaxing my body but stimulating my mind which *distracted* it – another Pain Management strategy – from the pain, whilst simultaneously attempting to keep my neurones functioning. I had no problem with having a lie-down or three throughout the day as part of my pacing regime, so long as my brain was occupied. Then I really could get away from the pain for a bit. So that became the strategy I adopted, not just for the duration of the programme, but for a long time afterwards.

Exercises were also a part of the programme. Gentle stretches and "circuit" exercises were introduced and you gradually built up the repetitions, or "reps", recording your progress daily in your folders. In fact you couldn't move on this course without ticking boxes, but it did help to structure things. Some of the exercises were similar to those on the Functional Restoration programme, but on neither course did the sheets of exercises explain in detail which muscles were being used or how muscles actually worked, knowledge I was sadly lacking.

Half way through the course we came to a session called "Challenging Thoughts." The occupational therapist gave us an excellent talk, which I can only describe as inspirational, about how positive thinking really could improve one's state of mind and combat negativity. If we think negatively, as chronic pain sufferers are frequently apt to do, we underestimate our strengths and resources and overestimate our difficulties. Positive thinking, on the other hand, can improve our outlook and help us achieve so much more. It had even been found that some holocaust victims had been able to think positively, a truly humbling notion.

Even having an upright posture could make people feel more cheerful, she said, whilst pretending to laugh could fool the brain into thinking it was the real thing and release the endorphins. She and her daughter had gone round all weekend going "ha, ha, ha" to each other, after attending a "laughter" event.

"You really have lost it, haven't you," said the physio.

"You'll be certified," called out one of the blokes.

But it didn't stop us all having a go at "ha, ha, ha-ing" to each other, which caused us all to start falling about with real laughter. This course was turning out to be rather fun!

Positive thinking encouraged me to draw a huge smiley face on a large piece of paper which everyone appreciated when I showed it the next time. I also went round sticking little smiley faces at strategic places round the house. I put one on the wall by my bed and it was the first thing I saw every morning. Most days it really did its job of making me start the day in a good mood, although there were inevitably bad days when I just wanted to tell it to bugger off. Somehow it managed to stay there despite my wildly fluctuating moods, until the bedroom was decorated five years later.

It's not always easy to think positively though. Anger, grief and sadness are valid emotions and it can't always be desirable to bottle them up. "Don't tell me how to feel," I used to sometimes want to scream. I know what they were aiming for, though. Constant negative thinking gets you nowhere. It makes you totally miserable and must drive those who live with you completely nuts. Leaning towards the positive, where possible, can't but help put you in a better frame of mind and stop you from sliding completely into the doldrums. To be fair we had a very understanding team and if someone was having a bad day and wanted to leave the room, have a good swear and kick a few walls it was recognised as a totally acceptable thing to do.

The way to adopt positive thinking, I decided, was to think small. Have a good reason to get out of bed. Enjoy the relief from the first pee of the day. Eat a really good breakfast. Do a few boring chores, and then lie down for my first relaxation session and distract myself with a Sudoku or other puzzle book.

It's not easy to think small, though, when you're someone who things in big projects, as I do. Ever since we'd moved I'd had Grand Plans for the house, such as knocking down walls, and putting in extensions. Or I'd wanted to "do" the garden, in a radical way – cutting down hedges, moving flower beds, re-doing the patio. I could do none of it. I was trying to forget about delphiniums, fuchsias and roses and learning to love my weeds instead.

A discussion of gardening came up in one of our sessions and we were told about a previous patient whose husband had built her a series of raised beds so that she could indulge her gardening passion. That's all very well, I thought, but you haven't seen the size of my garden. No way would that work for me. I no longer wanted to develop and indulge a passion for gardening; I simply didn't want the place to totally deteriorate.

We'd employed the first of a succession of gardeners in the summer of 2005. He turned up when he felt like it which was a bit disorientating and we were slightly relieved when he quickly passed us on to the second. This was a young chap who was very good, if rather slow, and worked for us for three years until he got a better offer – Highgrove! The third was an out-of-work building site manager who admitted cheerfully that he didn't know a lot about gardening. He was extremely pleasant, diligent and hard-working but dug up some of my favourite flowers along with the weeds. The fourth, who is more knowledgeable, came in 2010 and is still with us – he achieves twice the amount once a fortnight than others did once a week, so I hope he stays.

I adopted "acceptance of pain" as my Pain Management goal for the following week, having begun to get to grips with "relaxation," "pacing" and "positive thinking." I promised not to look for any more treatments or information on the internet for a whole seven days, but just to accept whatever pain I might have and use the skills I'd learned for coping with it. "Excellent!" they said. "You'll have more time to relax!" Having written it in my little box in my folder I had to stick with it – I knew I'd be grilled about it the following week.

You can't go for too long with a bad back before becoming aware that yoga and Pilates are often recommended as useful tools in the fight against pain. About halfway through the programme I asked the physio whether either of these would be suitable for me. She said that as I had a good amount of movement in my back, which was in itself good news, yoga or Pilates would be fine for me – they didn't count as "treatments." The reason they didn't want us having treatments was that they didn't want us wasting our money on things that probably didn't work. I didn't say anything, but as her colleague headed for the door, fag packet in hand, I reflected that there were worse things to waste my money on than treatments. Nobody was going to tell me what to spend my money on. I didn't waste it on smoking, booze or gambling, or spend it on luxury holidays, new cars and more clothes and shoes than I could possibly wear. I wanted none of these things, just my treatments which made me feel better, even if only temporarily, and which I was beginning to miss.

Fibromyalgia was a term that cropped up from time to time, and wanting to know more about it I borrowed a book from a woman suffering from it. I was pretty sure that I didn't have this debilitating condition but I came across the term "Myofascial Pain Syndrome" and looked it up – my week of not using the internet was now over – and read that the symptoms of this were tight fascia and widespread trigger points. In all the reading I'd done about trigger points I'd either not come across this precise term before, or had not taken it in. These symptoms fitted me absolutely. Was this the answer to my problems? Did I have other problems concomitantly? It didn't matter, I was told, if I didn't have an accurate diagnosis because I'd need the same Pain Management skills regardless. I didn't think that was satisfactory at all. If I didn't know what was wrong with me how could I possibly know whether I was curable or not? I wanted *answers*, I wanted them badly.

July came, although you'd never have known it. June had been the wettest on record and the forecast was not showing any improvement. We had no holiday booked as my pain made me reluctant to book anything, never knowing how I was going to feel from one day to the next. This makes forward planning very hard and I'd even begun to think that it wasn't worth having holidays at all. But this was hard on Ed and one day I decided to think "positively" and we booked a mini-break of three days on the Gower. Three days – surely I could cope with that? And if that went well perhaps we could find something else at the last minute.

Session ten of Pain Management was about "relationships," and was the opportunity it seemed for everybody to talk about their sex lives. But nobody wanted to – did I sense disappointment in the team leaders who'd clearly psyched themselves up for this? "Relationships" could mean many things and what people wanted to talk about was being irritable and upsetting their partners/friends/grandchildren etc. One of the blokes told a story of how he was having a quiet cigarette whilst looking after his grandson in a pushchair in the park and a passing woman said "Fancy smoking in front of a small child," and he told her to "eff off." He said he was ashamed, but he'd been in a lot of pain at the time. And I said she was being a busybody and asked what she actually did do. He said "She effed off!" and we all burst out laughing. People wanted to get things off their chest – somebody was in tears that she'd upset a friend by snapping at him. But everybody sympathised and in the end the session was extremely productive through enabling us to air and share our problems.

By session eleven the end was in sight. We were shown

how we could "progress" our exercises, and how we could safely get fitter, with activities such as brisk walking, swimming or cycling. "Flare-ups" were discussed and how we must be wary of "high-risk situations" which could cause stress and might stir up pain. What did we think might be a high-risk situation, we were asked? "Christmas!" I called out. We were reminded of all the skills we'd learned and which we could deploy at stressful times, because, as we were told "Pain Management skills are for life, not just for Christmas."

I decided to take the bull by the horns when it came to goal setting and announced my intention to go swimming. I hadn't swum since stirring up pubic symphysis pain in November 2005, but I was over that now and needed to face my demons. Afterwards the woman with fibromyalgia asked if she could come with me – she also had hurdles to overcome and going together would be mutual support. And so go we did. We swam widths – paced of course – with lots of rests, and didn't stir up any pain. Then we had coffee and quietly congratulated ourselves. We planned to go again after I'd come back from the Gower and perhaps make a regular thing of it and build it up. But the best laid plans of mice and men…

And so, on July 17th, we came to the final session. We started with an "exercise quiz," which we turned into a mock competition as we were all feeling a bit silly and de-mob happy. My team was very smug as we got all our answers right. After coffee we went over our action plans and then we re-scored our goals from the first week and wrote comments. All my scores had gone up. The goal sheets were photocopied and read by the staff, who said that everybody had improved, in different ways. They said we were a good group, a committed group. There were to be two follow-ups, the first in about three months' time and we set new targets to be gone over then. Then we each had to say one thing that we'd found particularly helpful and I said mine was challenging negative thoughts, but later, when I thought about it more, I wished I'd said something about the sharing of my experience of pain with the group. It had been wonderful to meet other pain sufferers – being in pain in the "normal" world is a very lonely place.

That was it, until the follow-up in October. We said goodbye and went our separate ways. We were on our own now to utilise all our newly acquired skills. How well would we all fare?

CHAPTER 7

If at First You Don't Succeed…

Continuing the Search

I had done everything the Pain Management team had asked of me – almost. I had paced and relaxed and done my exercises every day and set targets and goals and banished negative thoughts (mostly). But one thing I hadn't done – I hadn't given up on the little voice that said "There are still answers out there. Keep going and maybe you'll find them." Acceptance of pain, as prescribed by the PM team, didn't seem good enough. Of course I "accepted" it – living with it every day I had no choice. Long-term acceptance, which is what they really meant, was a different kettle of fish. Surely a balance needed to be struck between accepting it and looking for answers? Almost weekly, it seemed to me at the time, there were stories in the media of people defying their diagnoses and overcoming the odds stacked against them. I couldn't defy a diagnosis until I had one and I was going to keep going until I had.

By coincidence the day after the second anniversary of my injury (which I ignored entirely, not feeling nearly so buoyant as I had the previous year) I read an article about a man who had nearly lost his leg in a devastating mountaineering accident, but had refused to accept that he would never walk again despite having nine failed operations, had refused to have an amputation and had finally through his own will and determination won through. Not only had he walked again, he had returned to running and ten years after his injury had won a half marathon. Here was triumph over adversity indeed! Here was the inspiration I needed when the chips were down, to keep going with my quest.

My pain was getting worse again and in addition I was now failing to sleep. After three nights of what felt like coasting on the edge of sleep – what I later learned was "alpha" as opposed to "delta" sleep – I dug out the amitriptyline pills, which I had been off for many months and knocked myself out with them. I was able to get repeat prescriptions easily enough and was happy enough to take low doses of a drug that Dr Davidson had said was "so good they should put it in the water," but I was left with the question – why did I need it? Something else now seemed to be wrong – it felt to me as if my body had some kind of chemical imbalance. What was going on now?

At least I could get help for my sore aching body. Nobody could tell me not to have treatments any more. I resumed my Rolfing with Charlotte who had now returned from Hawaii. She might not have the answers as to the *cause* of my problems, she might only be treating symptoms, but boy, did I need my symptoms treating. This was not about cure – this was about pain relief. I arrived once again covered in bruises, from desperate attempts to eradicate trigger points with my rubber ball. She spent the whole session on my back. So many bits were tight and some muscles when she worked on them just would not glide smoothly but kind of jumped. They were like rope, she said. And my ribs were "shrink-wrapped" by fascia. "This is old stuff," she said, "It's not from your recent problems. Did you use to ride? I've met this before with horse riders."

Well yes I did, but even more significant, when I thought about it, was that I used to play the piano for up to five hours a day when I was a music student, and varying amounts ever since, keeping my arms held in the same unnatural position. Nowadays much more attention is paid to posture for musicians, with courses on Alexander Technique given to students and muscular tension in musicians being studied by medical professionals, but I'd never heard of any of that when I was studying.

I will never forget how wonderful I felt after that session with Charlotte. I was floating on air! I felt loose and flexible everywhere she'd worked and more relaxed than I'd ever felt in my entire life. I was euphoric with the lightness of my body to the extent that I wondered if it was even safe to drive home! No way was I going to give this up if it made me feel this good! I had one more session with her in which she worked hard to release the spasms that I complained of in my bum and thighs, before Ed and I left for South Wales.

We had one rare fine day in that most miserable of summers which we spent on the glorious Rhossili Bay, before heading back home again in response to a phone call from our neighbours back in Gloucestershire where the rain, which had set in again and was reaching Biblical proportions, was flooding the whole county and threatening our home. Due to their heroic efforts our house had only very minor damage and we were lucky compared with many others. It took us seven hours to get home, of which four were spent covering the last twenty miles as we drove through one flood after another, but we did get home that night. We saw tractors pulling cars out of floods, a policeman standing thigh-deep in water directing traffic and I lost count of how many abandoned cars we saw. We later learned that the M5, which we'd avoided, had closed and that all the people on it had ended up spending a cold, wet night in their cars.

There have been many floods and much distress since in this soggy island of ours, but our part of the country was not so badly hit again. People dined out for months on where they were in the great Gloucestershire flood of 2007. Many were forced from their homes and couldn't return for months. Among other things the Leisure Centre was severely affected and closed down for a year, so my plans for a weekly swim were scotched.

And then they turned the water off, because the water treatment centre was flooded and contaminated. For three weeks we had no mains water. A new word – "bowser" – entered our vocabulary, people fought over bottled water in supermarkets and the army was sent to camp on Cheltenham racecourse and sort it all out. As far as we were concerned the distribution system worked well and we collected our bottles from the village hall daily, where a spirit of friendly camaraderie grew up. We also had plenty of water for non-drinking purpose from our overflowing water butts – very good for hair-washing, I discovered.

It seemed that with the great rainstorm of July 20th the skies had finally emptied themselves and some of August in parts of the country turned out to be rather fine. Family and friends came to stay and we walked and sat out and at last began to enjoy some summer weather. Then we did a house swap with my elder brother and his family as three days on the Gower, one of them very wet, didn't seem like very much holiday. While they enjoyed fine weather in our house we went to Suffolk for a week where a misty cloud of drizzle hung like a pall over the county for five days and where it was so cold and damp that we put the heating on and refused to venture forth. Ed glued himself to my brother's computer, I curled up with another Joanne Harris novel – "Gentlemen and Players" – and we resigned ourselves to the fact that summer was just not meant to come our way very much that year.

At the end of August I finally came to the end of my Rolfing series. It was supposed to have been ten sessions but I'd been such a wreck, that Charlotte had extended it to thirteen. My whole body had been worked and gone over, some bits of it several times, and Charlotte said she could now feel individual muscles in my legs, which had been like lumps of wood before. I said a fond farewell to her, thanking her profusely for all she had done for me. She hadn't been able to completely fix me and told me I could come back for top-ups in six months' time.

Although not completely right, I was for quite a few weeks much, much better and was able to enjoy four and five mile walks. I'm going to fight so hard to still have this, I thought, as one Sunday in early September I climbed a nearby hill – the longest ascent I'd done since the accident – stopping frequently to look back at the wonderful view over to the Malverns. Really it was only my back bothering me now, and a few aches and pains that came and went and which I usually managed to massage away with my rubber ball. It was up to me to keep my muscles supple by maintaining my exercises and perhaps try a regime such as yoga – recommended by both Charlotte and Rachel – or Pilates.

My first efforts with yoga, from a DVD, gave me tennis elbow, so that was the end of that. The DVD was stuffed into the back of a cupboard where it has remained ever since.

Next I tried Pilates, favoured by Danielle. I joined a beginners' class in the neighbouring village. I struggled to get the hang of the basic breathing techniques and couldn't do most of the other moves I was being asked to do. My back ached for two days afterwards so I ditched that as well.

Then in October I went to a gentle ladies only gym, the result of picking up a voucher at a Health and Beauty Show. To my surprise I found myself enjoying it. They had "toning" chairs with devices attached, which you operated to work out different muscles. You sat on each chair for only thirty seconds, and then moved, when told to by an irritating voice emanating from the sound system, to the next one, which had a different attachment and which worked a different muscle group. Alongside each chair was a metal plate that you jogged on gently, also for thirty seconds, to keep your muscles supple. The complete circuit took ten minutes and a good workout was to go round three times. So I joined as a member and between the beginning of October and the end of January I went twice weekly. I never harmed myself and I greatly improved my fitness. I really enjoyed my sessions and came away on a high. Despite my failure with yoga and Pilates it seemed that at last I'd found something I could do that didn't damage me and made me feel good.

On the 10th October I went to the Pain Management follow-up. Not everyone showed up, but those who did gave mixed reports. In general most people were still practising some of the skills and feeling they'd benefited from having attended the course, though one man was still in severe pain and nobody could lift his dark mood. There was to be a second follow-up in January but I was ill and couldn't go. And so I lost any chance I might have had of maintaining contact with like-minded people.

Also in October I had two Chavutti massages – recommended by Charlotte. This was a strange experience indeed! The therapist covered me in olive oil, held on to a rope strung across from one wall to another, and did foot massage of my back in long sweeping strokes. It didn't make my back better, in fact it seemed to make it worse, it was expensive and I hated the feel and smell of the olive oil. Why couldn't we have had nice aromatherapy oils?

In the October half-term Ed and I went to Hay-on-Wye, where as well as browsing all the bookshops we did some quite strenuous walking on Offa's Dyke Path. I wanted to make hay (oh, excuse the pun) while the sun shone, that is while my body was behaving. Who knew when it would get worse again? As it was my back was killing me, and tightness was creeping back into my bum and thigh muscles, but I did it anyway and felt elated by my achievements. The hotel had an indoor pool and sauna and I swam every day, believing swimming to be good for backs. Well it wasn't good for my back. Whatever was wrong with it wasn't going to be cured by swimming and I gave up all attempts to swim for months.

November saw me visiting a nutritionist. You can't say I

wasn't trying! I'd begun to wonder if all the pain-killers I'd guzzled and/or the pain itself, which I found so wearing, had drained my body of essential nutrients. Maybe that was why I had sleep problems. I'd begun to read that this might be the case, but trying to understand about vitamins and essential nutrients and how much you needed of each and what foods contained what proportion of each was yet another minefield and I couldn't cope with it. I needed another expert.

Sarah the nutritionist put me on to a number of supplements, the main one of which was magnesium, important she said for good sleep and also for proper muscle function. She recommended I have a hair mineral test and so I had three small locks of hair snipped off – the process causing my hairdresser to nearly seize up with anxiety – and flown in a tiny envelope to America – a bit OTT I thought – wouldn't London have done? – and analysed for nutrients. When the results came back several weeks later I was low in every single nutrient apart from calcium. Was low magnesium responsible for my tight muscles, I wondered briefly? No it wasn't, at least not on its own, although restoring the nutrients I'd lost certainly must have improved my health in many ways. Although I thought I'd always eaten healthily there was plenty more to learn and I actually stuck to Sarah's prescribed diet for quite a long time. After a few months I emailed with my progress and told her I was "still eating healthily-ish." Her reply came back, "I'm so glad you're still eating healthy fish."

A good diet and my activity at the gym helped me get fit and lose weight and I went down a dress size. (What a pity it didn't last!) And after a month of taking magnesium I was able to sleep soundly and come off amitriptyline again and stay off it for many months. So despite the constant back pain that autumn was quite a good time. I still had no answers as to why I had back pain or why my bum muscles still spasmed up and had almost resigned myself to living with the mystery – until that is I went to a routine chiropractic appointment.

Danielle had advised me to go every six months for check-ups. I'd not seen her since the end of February – although I'd had a session with Meg in May – but now she was back after her maternity leave, with lovely pictures of her beautiful baby daughter. She did some minor adjustments, including as usual my SIJ, but she seemed pleased with all the activity I was doing. Then she said that the practice had just recruited a sports physiotherapist to run back classes and she advised me to go. "We're getting very good results with people who have niggling back problems that just won't go away with anything else." Yup, that's me, I thought, as I struggled to get off her treatment table. I signed up straight away. I didn't know it then but I was about to get some of the answers I'd been trying to find for so long. What's more they were so simple I could have screamed.

CHAPTER 8

Switching Back On

Core Stability

Ever since Dr Davidson had told me my injury was similar to that which a footballer might sustain I'd been wondering about how to find a sports physiotherapist. Now at last I had one, Christine. What's more she'd been appointed by Danielle, which meant, in my book, that she came highly recommended. I met her at the end of November when I started yet another "programme" – this one called Back Tone. I was to have ten sessions at a reduced rate, because I was a long-term patient – oh indeed I was – of the Natural Health Centre.

My previous experience with physios had not been great. Now Christine was to restore my confidence in the whole profession. She was young, still studying for her MA, but I was impressed by both her manner and her knowledge and skills. The sessions were only half an hour and the first one disappeared with the inevitable history taking and assessment, leaving very little time for anything else. But I learned something crucial. I had lost my "core stability". And this was the answer to many of my muscular problems.

Christine said some of my muscles were tight as they'd taken over the work that my deep core muscles should have been doing. My core muscles, also called "stabilisers" or intrinsic muscles, which should be strong, had "switched off" – a situation not uncommon, she said, with people who'd had the kind of pelvic problems I'd suffered. I had a "muscle imbalance".

"Core stability is something to do with Pilates, isn't it?" I asked Christine, without really knowing where the question came from. I must have learned something from the one and only session I did in September.

"Yes," she replied, "I come from a Pilates background."

Her programme was to target and re-educate certain core muscles one at a time. I remembered how at Pilates I had lain on the floor and sucked in my pelvic floor and tummy muscles, so was slightly surprised when Christine said the number one set of muscles I had to get going were my gluteals. The gluteus maximus (large muscle in your bum) is, or should be, one of the strongest muscles in your body. It is responsible for holding you upright – your "engine," Christine said – and to get it going again she wanted me to start with buttock clenches.

"Buttock clenches?" "Yes." Well that couldn't be difficult, surely. I had to squeeze both "cheeks," then each one alone, alternately. "Blink, wink, wink" – Christine smiled. Sounded pretty easy. But no it wasn't. I couldn't do it. My gluteal muscles had totally switched off, opted out of any work whatsoever.

Over the course of the next week I slowly trained my brain to tell my gluteal muscles to blink, wink, wink. Never mind practising pelvic floor exercises at traffic lights, I was busy doing buttock clenches in supermarket queues! Gradually it began to come. After about a fortnight I was aware of having little pillars in my bum holding me up, which felt like a totally new sensation. I experimented with my stance a bit and noticed one evening as I was cooking supper that I was beginning to stand like a chef!

My upper body, though, was tightening up again and I craved massage. Nadine, responsible for sending me to Rolfing in the spring, had left and been replaced by Pat.

"How long has your back been like this?" Pat asked at my first session with her.

"Like what?"

"All tense and knotted."

I said I wasn't aware that it was. It was very disappointing – I'd only finished Rolfing in August, not to mention my two Chavutti massages.

Slowly, however, as my work with Christine progressed, understanding began to dawn. The sessions were officially half an hour, but in practice often only about twenty minutes, by the time I'd reported my progress – or lack of it – and she had noted it down. They always seemed rushed and I felt I couldn't achieve all that she or I wanted, but on almost every occasion she explained to me, so that it really began to get dinned into my thick skull, about "global" or "mobilising" muscles versus "intrinsic," "core" or "stabilising" muscles.

In addition to my gluteals, the muscles I was to retrain and strengthen were my transversus abdominis (TA) – a deep tummy muscle – and my internal obliques, whilst my poor "mobilisers", including the hamstrings, adductors, and quads, as well as my old enemy the piriformis, bane of my life, needed to work less hard. By attempting to mobilise *and* stabilise which they are not designed to do, these poor muscles had reacted by becoming short and tight thus causing pain and impairing function. I read up about it and found that this "muscle imbalance" is well documented and understood by physiotherapists and athletes – and lots of people it seemed, except me.

Why had it taken two-and-a-half years before anyone had properly explained it to me? I felt frustrated and angry. Some of the exercises I was now being given were similar to the "circuit" exercises I'd done at Pain Management and at the Functional Restoration programme the previous year. And I had done them and done them. I was still completing daily tick boxes on the charts given me at Pain Management when I started Christine's programme. But not once had any of this stuff ever been really explained and for all that I knew I could well have been doing all the exercises wrongly. Without the proper rigorous focusing on the correct way of using my body – the training of my gluteal muscles, the strengthening of my abdominals – which I was now learning from Christine, I might not have achieved very much at all from my daily dozen. Maybe I'd missed something, but I doubted it. I felt I'd always paid close attention to the instructions I'd been given on both programmes. Christine's course was an education in itself and I began to regard what I was learning as just as important as the exercises themselves.

As with all such programmes Christine's exercises had to be paced and built up slowly over a period of time, but despite a few setbacks, I did begin to improve and could feel those deep stabilising muscles really beginning to work. In addition to bum squeezes and floor work, she added in Swiss ball exercises and later "wall-flattening" as she said I had too much curve or "lordosis" in my lower back. I often spent up to an hour a day doing all that she set me so I dropped going to the gym. Apart from anything else I didn't know if I'd been doing my work-out there correctly. It seemed much more sensible to do the exercises that were specifically targeted for my problems. I'd enjoyed the gym though and always intended to go back, but when I tried to several months later it had closed down. This gym had particularly suited my needs and I wasn't sure I could find anything else comparable at the time.

Over the Christmas break I began to take stock of things. The more I thought about it the more horrified I was that I had been overworking so many muscle groups in my legs and back. This had to be significant. I knew that I had walked badly at the beginning after the injury, but I had no idea I'd been doing it for so long. And recently! I thought of the trip to the Black Mountains where I had done two long walks of several hours, with hundreds of feet of ascent. How badly had I used my body then? Without the understanding I had now gained I might have carried on doing it forever, and Cindy could stand on me as long as she liked and Charlotte could Rolf me till the cows came home – I would end up undoing their work. No wonder I hadn't got better in two-and-a half years! Had I negated the effects of all my massages and Rolfing? And worse, what further damage might I have done that I hadn't yet discovered? I was soon to find out.

But before I did I felt able, for the first time in three years, to take part in the local traditional New Year's Day walk, or rather climb, to the top of Cleeve Hill. Up to sixty people, from small children to the eighty-year old leader, took part. It was my first serious walk since starting my Back Tone programme and I tried consciously to employ all the right muscles. On the whole I felt that I did and although my legs felt tight my back was definitely feeling quite good, so I must have done something right. My spirits soared. Could I dare to hope for a better quality of life in 2008 than in the past two years? I spent a long time talking to a chap who told me all about the walking he'd done in the Tirol the previous summer. Ideas began to form in my mind. It was years since we'd been abroad and I'd always loved Austria. In particular I'd always longed to go to Vienna. Would I be up to a more ambitious holiday this year? Would I be able to cope? I made a promise to myself that if I was still doing well by May I would dare to plan us a trip to Austria.

When I went back to Christine at the beginning of the new year – 2008 – I told her that I felt my back was definitely improving, but that my legs were really painful and after I'd done some poking around I had discovered they were very, very tight on the outside. This was a new discovery. Was the tightness here referring to other muscles in my thighs, all of which seemed painful? What was causing this tightness? Christine prodded me exactly where I indicated and her eyes lit up.

"You've got trigger points in your ITB," she said.

"In my what?"

"ITB. Iliotibial band. It's a very tough band of tendon that goes down the outer thigh. It's obviously been doing the job of holding you up that should have been done by your core muscles."

She had me lie on a mat on the floor and she reached for

84

a large sponge roller and started to massage my legs with it – almost like rolling out a sheet of pastry. I nearly shot through the roof. The pain was as intense as anything I'd known in the whole of the last two-and-a-half years. And the left side was as bad as the right. No way could I stand this. Was this the only way to get rid of these trigger points?

"I can release them with acupuncture," Christine said. "But you'll need three or four appointments." Yes, I'd have them! Delighted that she could offer this as well as all her other skills I booked the sessions up then and there and I went for the first of them two days later. We hadn't done any back exercises this time but such a significant discovery had been made that I felt it was one of the most important sessions of all.

More acupuncture. More needles. Here I go again. Never mind, acupuncture's not that painful. So I thought until Christine stuck her needles straight into the knots in my iliotibial band. It was *not* nice! It was horrible! It was right up there with Rolfing on my personal Painometer. She found about three or four places on each thigh where there were tight bands of muscle and stuck what seemed like handfuls of needles into each. Every time a needle went in I gave an involuntary jerk – this was the "twitch response" that you get with trigger points. And then the muscles seemed to grab the needles and close tightly round them. This went on over and over again, with each needle inserted. Then I lay there on my tummy for a while, looking like a pin cushion, while Christine did deep pressure with her thumbs into my piriformis. I was certainly getting the works all right!

Afterwards I felt as if arrows had been driven into my

thighs. But my back was great! It really felt as if it was no longer tied to my bum with string. The second session was only marginally less nasty than the first. In the third session she needled my tight hamstrings as well. I worked out that I had about six needles in each ITB and six in each set of hamstrings – twenty-four in all. Not a lot of fun.

The internet has plenty to say about "ITB syndrome." It appears it's common with runners – all that pounding on hard surfaces takes its toll on the legs – and to a certain extent with hikers. Given all the walking I had done – badly I now realised – in 2007, I couldn't be surprised that I had developed this painful condition. It usually causes knee problems. My knees were actually two of the few places in my body that were not causing problems, and I hoped they weren't going to start. I didn't want to be a runner, but I did want to do my walking.

Although I hated it, this "sports acupuncture" did improve my legs week by week and Christine could feel my muscles turning from taut "guitar strings," as she termed them, to something with a bit of elasticity in them. After the four acupuncture sessions as well as the continued core stability programme I was a different person. And yet...and yet... I still wasn't right. I was beginning to get a return of that over-all tightness that I now recognised as fascial. Christine was puzzled. She'd tried so hard with her Back Tone Sessions and all the acupuncture, and so had I, with all the exercises.

I decided that, once I'd finished my back classes I'd have some more Rolfing. It was nearly six months since I'd finished the "ten series" and I was "allowed" to have top-ups now. Maybe this time it would be even more effective now that I was, I hoped, using my body correctly. I'd emailed Charlotte over Christmas and discovered that she'd moved to Wales. However, she rang me to say that she was coming to Cheltenham in a few weeks to finish a few remaining sessions with other patients and she would kindly come on afterwards and give me three "top-ups" at home.

By early February I wondered if my core stability had improved enough to enable me to do some gardening – always the biggest test of both my back pain and my tight muscles. For half an hour I knelt on all fours weeding, whilst pulling in my deep abdominals as much as I could. At the end of this time I got to my feet with my back nearly killing me. This is ridiculous, I thought, don't be such a wimp. I leant vigorously backwards in a McKenzie extension stretch. Pain shot down from my armpits to my knees, as if Elastoplast had been ripped off both my sides. This had to be myofascial – I knew nothing else that hurt like that.

My last session with Christine was the following day. I was sad to say goodbye to her, knowing how much she'd helped me and how much I'd learned from her. However, she promised to give me acupuncture from time to time if I needed it, so it would not be goodbye forever.

Immediately after leaving her I went through a bad patch. Pain had gone from my sides but was now raging down my inner thigh. Had I strained my adductors again? If so, how? I couldn't put my foot to the floor without strong pain. There was nothing for it but to resort to PRICE – pills, rest, ice, compression, elevation.

I encouraged Ed to go out with the Ramblers on Sunday February 10th as it was the most beautiful bright sunny winter's day, and the Ramblers were walking locally. I'd join them afterwards at the pub for lunch, I said. While Ed was out I spent the morning on the computer sorting out my notes, writing up my pain diary again and thinking despondently that I would have to accept what they had said at Pain Management. I really would have to learn to live with my problems and adopt a different lifestyle, instead of constantly thinking that one day I would "get back to walking."

The Ramblers were nearly an hour late back to the pub for lunch, which meant that I sat in the car park for that amount of time, listening to Classic FM and watching the whole world walk past – couples, families, and groups – everyone from infants barely able to toddle to old men with sticks. I was fighting back the tears – why could all these people walk and not me? What had happened to me since conquering Cleeve Hill on New Year's Day?

By the end of the day I'd made a decision. I'd had so many problems but at the moment it was my leg that was hurting, my leg that was the problem. I was aware that despite the success at Back Tone, despite the improvement in my ITBs after Christine's acupuncture, I'd had tight, painful adductors for months, and now I had a real flare-up. There was real pain from a real cause there, I was sure – it wasn't just "referring" from somewhere else. Christine had been specifically employed by Danielle for the Back Tone programme and wasn't available to me as a general physiotherapist but a new physio – a really decent one – was what I needed. I was going to find the best in town.

CHAPTER 9

Joined-Up-Thinking

Physiotherapy and the Sarah Key Back Method

My work with Christine had restored my faith in the physio profession. I was also a bit more savvy now. After a lot of internet research I came up with Jan in Cheltenham who seemed to have many strings to her bow and had treated Olympic athletes. Surely she had to be one of the best physios around? Ironically she worked at the first physiotherapy centre I had attended more than two and a half years ago. I had come full circle.

Jan was of slight build, with short cropped hair and a business-like but pleasant manner – exactly as I envisaged a physiotherapist to be. I saw her on the 15th February when she listened to my story and read my notes of the whole past two and a half years, which I'd spent days reducing to two sides of A4. She said she didn't think my groin and thigh pain was the *cause* of my problem. She wanted me to have a full assessment with her and a colleague, Angela. She felt my whole body should be looked at, not just bits of it. This was joy to hear! The whole of the session was spent talking and discussing the possible problems and the options, and she told me to go away and think about it. I didn't need to think for long, but by the time I'd rung back to book another appointment the earliest one available was the 26th.

A few days later I cleaned and tidied the sitting room as Charlotte was due for the first of my Rolfing top-ups. The weather was cold and frosty and we'd had a log fire the night before. I cleared out the ashes from the grate and went out unthinkingly in my slippers to throw them onto the rose bed. I took two steps off the patio onto the lawn, skidded on the frost and felt myself falling, with my right foot slipping uncontrollably away from me, and my left buckling under the rest of my body. There was no doubt about it; I was doing the splits again. Even as I fell I remember thinking "Oh no, not my pubic symphysis, please not my pubic symphysis!" I sat there for a while not daring to get up, not wanting to know what damage I'd done. To do the splits once, I thought, may be regarded as a misfortune; to do them twice looked distinctly like carelessness.

Charlotte arrived in the afternoon and set up her treatment table in our living room. I'd forgotten two things about Rolfing – one: how horrible it is at the time and two: how great you feel afterwards. I told her how my fascia had pulled so horribly when I'd done a back extension exercise recently. So she worked all around my ribs, where I'd been "shrink-wrapped" before. And also around the hips and shoulders. I was tight again in all these places, but felt freer afterwards from her work.

As the days went by my back began to hurt in a way that could only mean something was "out." There was no doubt in my mind that I'd done something in that fall. Normally I would have gone rushing back to Danielle for this, but I had my appointment booked with Jan and Angela for the following week and I grinned and bore it until then. I didn't know it at the time but this latest cloud was about to have a silver lining.

Angela was beautifully turned out without a hair out of place. Like Jan she was enviably slim and fit-looking despite having – I later discovered – five children. Jan had passed on my notes to her, and her first comments to me when I arrived for the assessment were that she'd read them thoroughly, they were extremely helpful, she'd been able to make a partial diagnosis from reading them and she wished everybody else would come as well prepared! I was delighted and astonished – maybe the hours I spent maintaining my pain diary weren't wasted after all. To these notes I orally added the details of my recent fall and back pain.

The assessment that followed was one of the most thorough I'd ever had. I stretched up, I stretched sideways, I bent down, I stood on one leg and then the other and I lay down on a treatment couch and let Angela palpate numerous bits of me. She came up with the following diagnosis. My right sacroiliac joint had slipped upwards (*again*), jamming the lower vertebrae (L4 and L5) and the lower facet joints. The quadratus lumborum muscle, which joins the pelvis to the ribs, had gone into spasm and was preventing a lot of the other muscles from working properly. The misaligned SIJ was pulling all the muscles on that side up, making that leg functionally shorter. Her words! But I had used these words before myself, with no prompting from any practitioner. I was vindicated! This would probably explain why I had such pain in my right leg.

Jan, who was also present, conferred with Angela who went so far as to say she was "in no doubt" about her diagnosis.

She said she could correct my misaligned sacroiliac joint – she said it was an "upslip" – with a technique known as Muscle Energy Technique. She would also give me stretching exercises for my quadratus lumborum to prevent it from coming out again. If only! She would then manipulate and mobilise my spine and give me exercises, based on the work of the Australian physiotherapist Sarah Key, to free up the jammed vertebrae. She'd actually trained with Sarah Key, and was "very excited" she said, about what her work was achieving with backs. Even more heartening was her approval of Rolfing – she said it was one of the best things I'd done on my long list of therapies! The second top-up I had booked for the following Sunday would work well, she said, alongside what she would try to achieve, but she pointed out that fascia can get distorted again if the joints are stiff and the muscles unbalanced. Yes, I probably *had* undone a lot of Charlotte's good work of the previous year.

I mentioned something about the core stability work I'd been doing and Angela said, "You need to do everything. You need to have the sacroiliac correction *and* soft-tissue release of the quadratus lumborum *and* you need to stretch it *and* you need to strengthen your core muscles."

I could have wept. Joined-up thinking at last. Had I finally found my guru? Someone who could oversee a multi-disciplinary approach as I had so long wanted? Both she and Jan fretted over the fact that I'd not had a "global approach." But it hadn't been my fault. Over and over and over I'd been frustrated by not knowing where to go, who to ask for help.

"I'm fifty-seven," I said, remembering a comment from a friend that: "Youth was not on my side." "Fifty-seven is nothing," Jan replied vigorously, almost dismissively. "Now if you were eighty-seven it might be a little bit harder…"

"I thought your SIJ had been settled ages ago," Ed said when I arrived home and told him about my morning. It had been – for a while. But I wasn't surprised that it had come out again after my latest fall. I wasn't aware, however, that when it came out it jammed the facet joints and lower vertebrae. Had it done that before? That was a real, proper mechanical problem. There I was thinking it was just the muscle imbalance that was giving me the low back pain. And now I had a new muscle to think about – the quadratus lumborum (QL). Meanwhile Charlotte came for my second Rolfing top-up, in which she worked from the tips of my toes right up to my hips, and it felt good to tell her that her work was approved of by a main stream physiotherapist.

Angela started her work on me on March 4th. The Muscle Energy Technique (MET), when performed on me at least, turned out to be a form of traction. In time with my breathing she literally pulled my leg downwards, giving it a slight twist at the same time. She did it about three times, and then gave me ultrasound on my quadratus lumborum to break up the scarring, she said, and then she did the leg pulling again. Finally were the exercises – all for different things. A quadratus lumborum stretch, Sarah Key's "Rocking knees to the chest" to begin to get my spine unjamming, and "Knees passing" (core work) for my deep abdominals and my multifidus, a deep back muscle. At the end of it I got off the treatment table and immediately my back felt better – that had never happened before. I could tell straight away that the SIJ was now in place.

I did my new exercises assiduously. I knew a bit about

Sarah Key, who specialises in backs and has published several books. Two years previously I had bought her "Back Sufferer's Bible," after being recommended it by a retired physio I had met socially. I had tried some of the exercises, but hadn't got on very well with them. Now, however, I felt that doing them as part of a package under the guidance of an experienced physio I might get real benefit from them. The basic premise behind most of them is to get the spine to unjam and the muscles to unspasm for starters and then to do strengthening work on the abdominals.

After I'd practised "Rocking Knees to the Chest" for ten days Angela sold me a "back block" – basically a lump of wood – and told me to lie with my back extended over it for one minute a day. This would decompress my spine. I hated it but persevered. I persevered also with my quadratus lumborum stretches which had to be modified, because the first one I was given in which I crossed my right leg over my left and half fell off the bed, stirred up pain in my groin. It was hard to win. Instead I now sat on the coffee table and bent forward and sideways till my right elbow rested on my left knee. It was hard at first but I improved with practice and it did me good.

When Charlotte came for my final top-up I asked her to work over the quadratus lumborum area again. She got in deep around my "shrink-wrapped" ribs again – she said it felt as if my 11th and 12th ribs on the right side were stuck together. The whole area felt to her like rubber. "This is stuff from years ago," she said again – all that piano playing? – and I knew it wasn't going to be undone in one or two sessions. Despite the brutality of the treatment I felt that I still wanted more work on the same area. Every day, until it finally unglued!

That was the end of my three top-ups and I knew it was the end of treatment with Charlotte. She couldn't continue to keep driving up from Wales. As with Christine I felt sad to see her go; she'd done me so much good and kept me functioning at a level I couldn't have dreamt of if I'd been untreated.

By the end of March Angela felt my sacroiliac joint was stable enough for her to start doing serious work on my back. True to her word she started to mobilise my spine with her foot. It felt good, as if things were really starting to move. She now asked me to use the back block twice a day and to increase and progress my exercises further. They would help, she said, to "gap the spine open", free up the nerve root and stop the muscles contracting. The QL was freeing up although there was still a way to go. I asked about massage and she referred me on to the clinic's own massage therapist, Kim. It was Kim who had given me my first massage ever, two and a half years ago, when she had worked at my local Natural Health Centre. Once again I felt I had come full circle.

Of course not everything was straightforward – it never was. One evening when I was in a lot of pain and suspected that my SIJ had come out again, I got Ed to do a DIY version of traction on my leg. I felt great afterwards! Four days later I got him to repeat it and although this time he probably overdid it and left me feeling very sore, I took ibuprofen and felt better the following morning.

A fortnight went by and it was quite a good fortnight. I enjoyed my massages with Kim – how lovely it was to have treatment that is really nice to receive *and* which does you good! With all the Rolfing I'd had massage now was not nearly as painful as when I'd had that first session with her over two years previously. I began to pace up my walking again, although I was aware of things not being totally right in the SIJ – Ed's DIY treatment was not really the answer, I decided. We were now into the middle of April and I was due to see Angela again.

"Do you want the good news or the bad news first?" I asked her. I gave her the good news, which was that my spine felt much freer. When she checked she agreed; she said I was far less stiff and my facet joints were all moving nicely now. I told her the "bad" news about the SIJ and she made me do the "stork" test. She said it was up-slipping a little, then not moving down well, so she gave it her MET treatment. Then I confessed about Ed's DIY traction. She laughed with astonishment! She said she didn't think he could do any harm, which is what I'd thought. In general Angela was pleased with me. She said I should continue massage with Kim, but needn't see her for a month.

Kim was unerringly finding all my trigger points – in my neck, in my back and in my thighs. Oh those thighs! They were still full of the damn things, although Kim was working hard on my quads and my hamstrings. Tight hamstrings can contribute to back pain by tilting the pelvis too far up at the front. Tight quads on the other hand can tilt the pelvis too far down, also causing back pain. What is the effect if you've got both tight hamstrings and tight quads?

Despite everything improving, despite all my treatments, and all my exercises, I still had low back pain. It had however, become less frequent and since Angela had told me it would take between three and six months to really settle down I was not disheartened. I would keep on with my exercises and my back block and hope for further improvement. To "Rocking knees to the chest" I had now added "Rolling along the spine" – in other words "Rock'n'Roll"!

At the end of the month I did my first ramble for many months. I took a short cut at the end to avoid the steepest hill, but it was a lovely spring day and my hopes were high. I was in much better shape than when I'd merely had to watch people walking back in February. On the 18th May I rambled again, and this time completed the whole of the five miles. I then followed that by nearly an hour's gardening. I might not be completely pain free, but a large part of my function was restored.

May was to be a largely good month. I went to a school reunion – 40 years! – and had no pain all day. Probably it was because I was distracted with non-stop talking and listening, catching up on forty years of old friends' lives. Kim gave me the last of her series of weekly massages, which felt one of the nicest and most comfortable massages ever. I had two more acupuncture sessions with Christine – the first time I'd seen her for three months – and although she found plenty to needle, she said at the end that she thought my legs were in the best shape she'd found since she'd started working on them. We agreed I'd come back to her every three months for a maintenance programme, especially if I was going to do a lot of walking. This kind of targeted acupuncture seemed to me to do a pretty good job and if I had it once every three months that was only four times a year. I could stand that, especially if it gave me the freedom to walk.

At my last appointment with Angela on May 20th she said

there was no comparison between my back now and when she'd first started treating me at the beginning of March. My sacroiliac joint was stable, my quadratus lumborum muscle wasn't tight any more and as for my facet joints – they were loose and free whereas she said they'd been like "concrete" before. I could now Rock 'n' Roll till my knees reached my boobs. Angela mobilised me a bit with her hand and then her foot and then asked me to try it out on her (she had a back problem too). "I could have you do that all day!" she laughed. She said I could massage my iliotibial band trigger points in my thigh myself, though not with a rolling pin (now how did she know I'd tried that?) I told her I normally used a rubber ball against the wall – I was able to stand this now for short periods – and she said "perfect." She said ITB trigger points were notoriously difficult to get rid of and I said I had a small hope that if my core stability improved and I got rid of them they wouldn't come back. "Oh no they won't," she said. "You won't have them for life. You'll be pain free!"

Did I dare to believe her? She gave me additional exercises to further my progress and said it should take about six months for core stability to be restored. I'm well into that, I thought, though as I'd had stops and starts at the beginning I couldn't really say when the six months began. She suggested I went back in three months' time for a check-up, but otherwise I was "signed off." What a lovely feeling!

The only trouble was, I still had pain and some days it was quite bad. My leg pain for example – that pulling, tight feeling in my inner thigh and groin which came and went and sometimes made walking extremely difficult – which had brought me to Jan and Angela in the first place. Oh well, I thought, it would probably go away soon – it was probably something that had "referred" from somewhere else and would sort itself out now that other bits of me appeared to have been fixed, and if I continued with the exercises.

Unfortunately I spoke too soon. Something was still very wrong. The joined-up thinking hadn't quite joined all the dots yet.

CHAPTER 10

Untangling the Web

Myofascial Release

It was the May half-term and I'd not forgotten my promise to myself that we'd go to Austria for our summer holidays and now was the time to get down to some serious planning. A really decent holiday, after the appalling summer of the previous year, would do wonders for my morale, I knew. I sat in the garden and planned our Grand Austrian Tour. We decided to do a rail trip, taking in cities and mountain scenery. Sitting and watching the landscape go by, being able to get up and stretch and walk up and down the train if I needed – that was the way to go. I spent hours poring over brochures and trawling the internet for train timetables and hotels, deriving almost as much pleasure from the planning as I later did from the trip itself.

Concerned, however, about renewed tightness in my body, I started wondering again about Myofascial Pain Syndrome, which I'd first come across in the book lent to me when on the Pain Management course. More internet research led me to another, larger and more detailed book called "Fibromyalgia and Chronic Myofascial Pain," which I ordered and which arrived at the very end of May. It was to become my new Bible.

I read it avidly, I devoured it. It described in great detail what fascia is, its importance, and what happens right down to the cellular level in our bodies when it gets restricted. There is a similarly detailed chapter devoted to trigger points. It is written by a medically trained person who herself suffers from both myofascial pain and fibromyalgia – so she knows her subject from both sides. I couldn't take it all in, but there is enough of it written in plain simple language for the layperson to understand. After reading how the symptoms of fibromyalgia are differentiated from those of "Myofascial Pain Syndrome," which is now called "Chronic Myofascial Pain" or CMP, I decided that I definitely didn't have the former, but I was pretty certain I did have the latter.

What to do about it? According to my book, which was American, the medical profession in America is largely untrained in the diagnosis and treatment of this condition and I didn't expect it to be any better here. Not one doctor I'd seen had mentioned the word "fascia" to me. But *I* believed in fascia and fascial restrictions and the pain they could cause, especially after my experience with Rolfing, and this book gave me new confidence that my belief was not misplaced. I was suffering from something real.

As if to prove it my inner thigh/groin pain had returned after a walk and I had trapped a nerve in my left calf after doing some gardening. At least I thought that's what it must be. Initially I felt as if I'd been knifed and thought that perhaps I'd been stung by a bee or knelt on a thistle, but no dead bees or squashed thistles in the vicinity could show this to be the case. This was no good. Austria was booked and paid for now and the Eurostar tickets had arrived. It was vital that I be able to walk. To go to Charlotte in Wales, have treatment and return would take a whole day, but I almost considered it. Then I read in my book about Myofascial Release, based on the work of the American physical therapist, John F. Barnes. I'd come across his name before and now looked at his website. It doesn't mince words. Barnes is described as an "icon" and a "trailblazer". Patients are referred to his treatment centres from all over the world when traditional therapy, medication, or surgery had failed to produce the desired results. Myofascial Release has "exploded on the therapeutic scene with an unprecedented impact and is considered the most effective form of therapy in the history of healthcare!" Bold claims indeed! Barnes has also been responsible for the training of many thousands of physicians and therapists, one of whom, happily for me, had brought his work to the UK. I had to try this therapy, even if the extravagant claims should be taken with a pinch of salt.

Ruth Duncan, based in Glasgow, calls her approach "Integrated Myofascial Therapy." In addition to her own practice she also runs courses and her website had a list of practitioners whom she'd trained, working in different parts of the country. The nearest one to me was Jill, in Kings Heath, Birmingham. It would mean a round trip of eighty miles – a bit different from driving the short distance into Cheltenham. But my holiday was only six weeks away and I had days when I was struggling, yet again, to walk. At least Kings Heath was the near side of Birmingham. I rang Jill and, after a short chat with her, booked an appointment.

How glad I am that I did! Myofascial Release freed me up as only Rolfing had done hitherto, and what's more it did it almost painlessly. I couldn't believe how wonderful this treatment, which it had taken me three years to discover, made me feel. Why isn't it better known?

Initially I found it very strange. For the first half-hour or so it seemed to consist of Jill waving my legs in the air. OK, it was done in a very controlled way, starting with small movements which grew bigger and in which the legs were slowly turned both inwards and outwards more and more. But bizarre, nonetheless. Jill could tell from this, however, the state of my fascia, and she said it was "solid." That sounded a bit grim, especially after all my Rolfing. I knew, now, however that I had probably undone the Rolfing work and no longer regarded it as solving problems for life. If I still had a muscle imbalance this would inevitably cause my fascia to tighten.

In order to release the psoas and other hip flexors Jill now placed one hand on my thigh and the other on my abdominals, and then, whilst exerting gentle but firm pressure, very slowly allowed them to move apart as the fascia began to stretch. A slight burning sensation accompanied this work, but the rest of the treatment was completely painless and very pleasant to receive. Was this really it? Was this what the great John Barnes had discovered? I drove home unsure about it all. But as with all therapies I knew you had to give them several sessions to reap real benefit. I ended up having five before going on holiday.

The second session felt as if a bit more was achieved. After my legs had been waved about and my psoas released, I turned onto my tummy for Jill to do piriformis work. My leg was put into some extraordinary positions and gently stretched every which way, but always under Jill's control. The aim was to get the fascia to be free in all directions. Unlike Rolfing nothing was ever forced – everything was done slowly with the aim of getting the fascia to gradually unwind by itself. Well, if this was going to be as effective I'd rather have this any day – I'd never want Rolfing again! I was asked to stretch my piriformis every day by lying on my tummy and doing "frog" stretches – moving my knee out to the side and then pushing it upwards. "When you've got it up to your ear you'll know your piriformis is nice and loose!" Jill said.

We were into July by the time of the third session. My holiday was only twenty days away. Once again my psoas was worked on. And I knew definitely that it was fascial tightness here that had caused that terrible tension and pulling sensation in my right thigh and groin, which had plagued me on and off all year and prevented me walking. After each session it loosened that little bit more – Jill said there was much more "give" in my right leg now. She said that if the fascia was tight round the pelvis it put a strain on all the thigh muscles and I said that described exactly what I felt.

In session four I understood why the treatment was called Integrated Myofascial Therapy. Myofascial Release was integrated with other treatments, such as massage and soft tissue release. By now Jill was focusing more on my upper body, although she always started the sessions with the leg and psoas work. My shoulders were tight again and that's where a lot of my back pain was coming from. One of my upper back muscles felt particularly tight and twangy. "You could play a tune on that one," she said. She massaged my upper body for about half an hour, and then sent me away with yet more exercises to do. I did them all – I thought they were brilliant.

After my last session in which she gave my whole body a thorough going over two days before leaving for the Continent, I left her clinic feeling lighter and freer from top to toe. I got into the car and started my journey home – by now I was used to the hour's drive and even enjoyed it. I drove back floating on air, singing along to Mozart on the radio and as I hit the dual carriageway I soared to top F with ease. Top F! – I'm normally an alto going on tenor. But today I was on top of the world! Today I was flying! My body felt wonderful and my holiday was only days away. I was going to Vienna, to Salzburg – Mozart's birthplace – and then to the mountains. I was going to have the holiday of a lifetime and Jill had made it possible. No wonder I was singing!

I was happy as I packed my holiday clothes, also apprehensive. Unlike the holidays of the last three years I couldn't just get in the car and drive home if I had a pain flare-up. I had assembled and packed a pain management kit – painkillers, TENS unit, Tubigrip for thigh support, rubber ball for trigger point massage, and – my latest acquisition – a Paingone pen, a handy device which is supposed to relieve trigger point pain although I never found it much use. Despite all this paraphernalia I still felt anxious. But I was going and that was that. I was in the best shape I'd been in since the injury – surely I'd be able to relax and have a good time?

The packing done I did some fairly thorough vacuuming, at the end of which I had such a backache I didn't know what to do. I simply couldn't understand why I still got back pain. Angela had stabilised my SIJ, freed up my spine and I'd been doing her exercises as well as Christine's for five months now.

My gluteal muscles were in good shape, my obliques were firm and my transversus abdominus was now so strong you could have walked on it. "You'll be pain free" – I remembered Angela's words. But I wasn't. What was going on? Why did I still get back pain?

Some instinct told me to abandon Sarah Key flexion exercises and do McKenzie extension ones instead. So I lay on my tummy and arched my body backwards and it sent the pain away. It was risky starting a new regime two days before going on holiday, but whatever was going on in my back, this worked.

I did McKenzie extension exercises along with a regime of stretching every day of the holiday. With my myofascial system freed up I now welcomed the stretches I had once so hated. From tiny hotel rooms like the one we had in Brussels, where there wasn't room to swing a cat, to the spacious suite we had in Vienna, I rocked, rolled, arched backwards and gently stretched before leaving the hotel every morning.

Fate smiled on me. We sat on trains watching fabulous scenery go by, sometimes for up to five hours at a time, with scarcely a twinge of stiffness. I braced my body as Danielle had taught me years ago and hauled my suitcase on and off the trains with no trouble at all. We tramped round cities and towns – Brussels, Aschaffenburg, Vienna, and Salzburg – seeing all the sights, getting nothing worse than "museum feet." Vienna was as wonderful as I'd hoped, Salzburg unbelievably beautiful. We visited palaces and castles and exhibitions and parks and markets, and spent a whole day at the two Mozart museums. We took a boat trip on the not-so-blue Danube and went to a concert in the Schönbrunn Palace and saw "The Magic Flute" performed by the famous Salzburg marionettes. We ate the biggest Wiener Schnitzels in Vienna, had *Kaffee und Kuchen* in the Café Landtmann, Freud's café, and drinks in the *Schwarze Kameel* (Black Camel) once frequented by Beethoven. I posed with a huge silly grin on my face in front of statues of Mozart, Beethoven, Schubert and Strauss. The sun shone every day out of a cloudless sky, my muscles were warm and flexible and I was as happy as I'd ever been.

Then we went to the Alps. In Zell-am-See, armed with two walking poles, I climbed 1500 feet up into the mountains, then down again, pacing it with many breaks, but still I did it. We hired bikes and rode all the way round the lake with no problems at all. In Mayrhofen we took the gondola to the top of a mountain where the breathtaking scenery was heart-stopping. We went halfway down in the gondola to the middle station, and then walked back to the village. It took about four hours, walking on increasingly narrow and sometimes steep paths. Then I went swimming in the hotel pool. All with only the merest twinges of pain.

The journey back took us down the Inn Valley, via Bregenz to Lindau, a beautiful old town on an island in Lake Constance, where we stayed two days. Still the sun shone; still the temperature was thirty degrees most days. England meanwhile had another exceedingly dull August. And, unlike last year, I had missed it!

We began to catch some of the bad weather when we arrived in Strasbourg in pouring rain. We had only a few hours here but we saw as much as we could of the beautiful old town, with the rain pelting down on our umbrellas and swirling round our feet in the cobbled streets. I got cold and wet but still I didn't suffer. Finally, after nearly three weeks away, we went home via Paris.

With us was a camera full of stunning photos and a whole bank of fabulous memories of our wonderful trip, off which I was to feed for at least the next six months. I was so glad I had them – beyond glad – because the next six months were to prove very difficult indeed.

CHAPTER 11

Shaping Up

Pilates and Posture

On the very last leg of our tour I picked up a text from one of my brothers saying our mother had had a fall the previous week, the second time it had happened when I was on holiday. I rang him and heard that she had bumped her head badly. Although she was badly bruised an X-ray had shown nothing, and since there was nothing either he or I could do he kindly hadn't told me until I was nearly home.

She was never really to recover from that fall. At first she seemed fine, and amazingly was in no pain and, as was the case two years previously, she had no recollection of falling or of going to hospital for an X-ray. She couldn't see herself and couldn't understand the reaction of visitors who exclaimed, "You *have* been in the wars!" or words to that effect. In fact she seemed exceptionally cheerful! But this phase was to be short-lived. She deteriorated rapidly and was soon transferred to the nursing floor. She ate little and became painfully thin. Her speech became hard to understand. I did manage to take her for one last outing on a warm day in mid-September. I took her in a wheelchair into the gardens. I pushed her round showing her all the flowers I could find – she had always loved flowers. But now she showed no interest. I said wasn't it lovely to be out in the warm sun. "Sun – warm," she said. I never heard her speak again. She died peacefully at the end of the month, surrounded by members of the family, nearly all of whom had made it for a final goodbye.

The family all pulled together through the following busy days ahead and through the sadness of the funeral. Inevitably it was stressful and inevitably it stirred up physical as well as emotional pain in me, but there was no doubt that, despite the empty place left in my life, a big weight had been lifted from my shoulders. It wasn't all sad – the coming together of the extended family for the wake was a cheerful time of remembrances, chatting and laughter, which is what my mother would have wanted. She'd have been the first to join in.

We went to Scotland for a mini-break three days after the funeral. This had been planned long ago, but the timing of it couldn't have been better. Ed enjoyed himself at a school reunion, I became acquainted with a lot of his old friends I'd met only briefly before or knew only by name, and we had a chance to walk by the Tay and in the hills above Perth amidst glorious autumn colours. It was a great antidote to all the stress of the previous fortnight.

Meanwhile I had had two more appointments with Jill and my three-monthly ITB acupuncture with Christine in early September, wanting to make sure I dealt with any tightness that might have accrued from the exacting walking I'd been doing in Austria. "I hope you squeezed your glutes hard," Christine said when I told her I'd been climbing mountains.

Had I? I knew I'd stretched my hamstrings and quads repeatedly – before, during and after my walking. But I knew my core work had slipped, and knew that it was crucial for maintaining pelvic stability. It was time to have another go at Pilates, especially as Jill, too, swore by it. With the best will in the world it was sometimes hard to maintain a daily exercise regime when there's no one monitoring you or giving you any feedback. Christine was not available to me for this work but I found a Pilates teacher on the internet who sounded just right. She was very experienced and specialised, her website said, in the prevention and cure of musculoskeletal problems. This sounded great. I'd be able to tell her my history and work within my limitations. Perhaps I'd be able to take up with her the work I'd left off with Christine. I booked an appointment.

Her name was Marion, she had turned the whole ground floor of her house into one gigantic Pilates studio and she was one of the most intense people I have ever met. To start with I had an assessment. According to her my whole body stance was wrong. I was sticking my tummy out and had too much lordosis (curve) in my back, I was thrusting my head forward and causing tension in my neck and I was hunching my shoulders. I wondered if I was doing anything right. She'd never heard of trigger points which threw me rather, as by now I'd learned that most bodywork practitioners were familiar with them. I tried to tell her what they were, but it all came out wrong and I don't think she believed a word I was saying. As I continued with my story and showed her the exercises I'd done with other therapists there were tuts and sighs. This made me very defensive as I had become emotionally attached to many of my previous therapists seeing them as potential healers. She, in turn, clearly felt her expertise was under attack by my continual quoting of other people, though I felt that, as a professional, she should have been able to rise above this. This was a bad start – and that's before I'd even started Pilates.

I began to have doubts as to whether we would get on but Marion then told me about her training and her expertise – clearly very extensive – and said she was "passionate" that she could get me right. She wanted me to come for six individual sessions before joining a class and to cancel all other treatments. Despite some misgivings I agreed.

It was late October before I finally got started with her, the sessions having been put on hold due to my mother's death. She started by having me lie on a mat while she gave me various stretches. She stood over me and shouted "Pull your tummy in – breathe – stretch – point your toes – breathe – stretch – tuck your chin in – breathe! – stretch your arms – lower your shoulders – breathe! – stretch your toes – pull your tummy in – tuck your chin in – breathe, *breathe, BREATHE!*" She kept this up for nearly an hour – I don't know who was more exhausted at the end of it, her or me. Basically she had decided that I was the wrong shape and she was trying to make me stretch into the right one. I felt quite good after it, so went home and continued with one of the stretches – the star – which I felt was stretching my whole body at once and therefore not putting too much stress on any particular part of it.

Two more sessions followed in which she had me using some machines to improve my upper body alignment. She dinned into me the importance of not hunching my shoulders or sticking my chin out, because of the tension this causes in the neck muscles which feeds into the shoulders and then into the back. No doubt I had been told this before, but this time it went into my thick skull and stayed in for quite a while. I was free of upper body pain for a long time after this. What I couldn't understand, though, is why I was sticking my chin out in the first place – surely I never used to do that?

At the end of the third session Marion stuck me in front of a full-length mirror and cajoled and adjusted and pulled and pushed me into what she said was the perfect posture. My shoulders were down, my chin was tucked in, my abdominals were pulled towards my back, and my bum was pulled towards my front. Everything that could be pulled in was pulled in – I could hardly breathe. "There," she said, "You look beautiful." No I didn't, and I certainly didn't feel it. She stood next to me, lycra-clad, toned, slim, radiating health. Beside her I just looked like a pudding – dumpy, lumpy, frumpy and grumpy. I hadn't a hope of maintaining that posture without the aid of whale-bone stays.

Things got worse at my next session in early November. Both my thighs were really tight and sore and the new stretch she was asking me to do – I think it's called "Torpedo" or maybe it's "Diamond"– caused pain, especially in my hamstrings, and I was reluctant to do it. Marion's voice telling me to stretch through the pain was at war in my head with the voices from the Pain Management programme, which had said precisely the opposite. I stopped the exercise and told her I was not prepared to do it, and this seemed to annoy her. I was certainly no expert and didn't know exactly what was causing the tightness in my legs; I just knew that my body was telling me to back off. I'd stirred up pain so often in the past by overdoing things and I wasn't prepared to do so again. I can't remember what I said to ease the situation between us but somehow we made our peace and I booked up the next two sessions.

I was far from happy though. Despite her claim to work with injured people and work only at their pace I felt I was being controlled and pushed, almost bullied, beyond my comfort zone. I felt I was being asked to work against my body with all its limitations, rather than with it. Above all, I felt I was not being listened to. She had all the answers and I knew nothing. And whilst the latter was probably largely true what I had learned, after three and a half years, was when to stop. I returned home and emailed her and said I wouldn't be coming back. I felt sorry about it, because she had relieved my shoulder and neck pain, and I had actually learned a lot from her. I wanted to give credit where it was due.

I worked on my tight thighs again, massaging manually and with the ball. After a few days I had loosened things up a bit and thought perhaps I would give the "torpedo" stretch a try. Maybe it really would straighten my posture and improve the ever-present back pain. I lay on the bed and stretched and stretched and stretched and stretched. In the morning I woke up with severe pain in my groin – the worst I'd had for months. And in addition to the chronic backache I also had a strong and all-too-familiar deep ache on the right side of my pelvis. I knew without a shadow of a doubt that I had put my sacroiliac joint out again.

It had been stable for six months and pelvic stability was one of the reasons I had been able to enjoy the summer as much as I had. Angela's work – the pelvic corrections and freeing up of my spine – and Jill's myofascial release – the careful stretching of my soft tissues – all of which I had carefully protected for months, had all been undone.

I could have wept. I probably did – I certainly swore and kicked the bed and punched the pillow and raged against fate for its cruelty and against myself for my stupidity. I hadn't had a treatment of any kind for two months – Pilates is not a treatment – but this was something I couldn't fix myself. There was nothing for it but to go back to one of my practitioners.

What was it that made me decide to go back to Danielle, in the first instance, rather than Angela? Perhaps because Angela had "signed me off" and had been rather offhand, I thought, at my check-up. Perhaps I missed Danielle – it was months since I'd seen her and I'd always felt better just from seeing her warm welcoming smile. Often, even if her treatments hadn't held, chance remarks she had made had given me food for thought and opened up whole new areas of research for me. Whatever the reason I booked an appointment and went to see her on November 21st.

I was not to be disappointed. Once again I was to be struck by something she said. Unwittingly she gave me a key to opening a new door, a door that was to lead to real understanding of the *cause* of all my problems. I didn't know it then, but the following year – 2009 – was to bring about life-changing events.

CHAPTER 12

Striking Gold

Breakthrough

It was late November 2008 and life-changing events were
some way off. All I knew at the moment was that I had to get
out of the hole I was currently in. Danielle did the usual
chiropractic adjustments and said, depressingly, that my
sacroiliac joint was quite badly misaligned and my pubic
symphysis was "out" as well. I asked her if she thought I would
always have a problem with these joints and she said it was
quite likely because I had probably over-stretched the
ligaments that hold the joints in place and once over-stretched,
ligaments become lax and never quite recover. This remark
lodged in my brain and was to resurface some months later.

Meanwhile this treatment didn't hold and nor did the next
one and although she said I should come back for a third I
didn't. Instead I tried DIY treatment to pull in my own joints
and got Ed to do it, neither very successfully. So in mid-
December I went back to Angela who did her Muscle Energy
Technique on my leg and I felt better *straight away*. It seems
such a simple procedure but it's actually very skilled, with
exactly the right amount of rotation and traction exerted on
the leg, and timed exactly with my breathing. I asked her about
corsets, getting depressed that I was never going to keep my

pelvis in place without artificial aids. She recommended a lumbar corset, different from the SIJ one I'd bought some three years before. I ordered one in January and it became a valuable aid for the next three years.

I cosseted myself and did all the appropriate managing techniques I knew so well up to and over Christmas. By Boxing Day I was able to enjoy a gentle family walk. At New Year we went to a local barn dance – a new venture for the village. Walking was one thing, dancing quite another. I felt rather out of things as I sat watching everyone else gallop, and reel and do-si-do before me, but good came out of it because not only did we make friends with another couple sitting at our table, I found out that the woman was a fellow sufferer. She and I happily talked for a large part of the evening about misaligned sacroiliac joints and tight piriformis muscles and plenty else besides, leaving our husbands to listen in somewhat bemused silence.

It was now 2009. I bought a new book and started doing exercises to strengthen my multifidus muscle. "The multi what?" Ed said, "I haven't got one of those. What will you come up with next?"

The multifidus is a deep muscle running the length of your back and it's a crucial core muscle to strengthen if you have back pain. Angela had given me an exercise for it and "The Multifidus Back Pain Solution" by Jim Jonson was, at that time, number ten in Amazon's Top Twenty-Five Bestselling List. Clearly it wasn't only me who hadn't yet found the answer to back pain. The main exercise you were required to do was familiar – kneel on all fours and alternately lift one arm and the opposite leg. I'd been given it before. But now I did it rigorously, building up the repetitions and consciously "switching on" the multifidus muscle as Christine had taught me with my other core muscles. It did seem to be a missing link and certainly helped. I also learned to firm it up every time I got out of bed or up from a chair, so that I could stand up with my entire back moving as a whole, instead of swaying about like a willow blowing in the wind.

The only trouble was that it didn't cure my back pain. It did however lessen it for quite a while until the spring, when gardening brought it back again – in spades.

I also had a session of acupuncture with Angela's colleague Jan, having learned that she possessed this skill, hoping to free up some muscle spasm. Afterwards she gave me a stretch for my ITB. It involved crossing one leg in front of the other, and it sent my leg into spasm for hours, so I abandoned it and that was the end of that. Over the years I had been given several exercises that involved crossing one leg over the other – by Meg to stretch my piriformis, by Angela to stretch my quadratus lumborum and now this one for my ITB. Always they sent screeching pains down my right leg, but somehow I hadn't seemed to grasp that there was a pattern here.

The next day we got snowed in and any treatments I might have planned were put on hold. I decided to enjoy the snow. Why should the kids have all the fun? We had more snow than we'd had for years, the schools closed and the children took themselves off to the top of Cleeve Hill with toboggans and tea trays. Our lane was impassable and piano lessons were cancelled. I went round to the neighbours and asked, "Did you once tell me you had a sledge in your garage?"

"We've got a couple actually," they said expressing

astonishment when I asked if I could borrow them. "I'll cope," I said, "I'm determined to have a life."

In the end they came with us to one of the more gentle slopes nearby where we had a whale of a time – grown-up kids all. I was slightly more comfortable lying on my tummy on the sledge than sitting up, digging my toes into the snow behind me to brake. I went the whole length of the run several times, going a bit faster and getting a bit bolder each time. It wasn't easy to get myself down to ground level, harder still to get up and I was sore in lots of places afterwards but I had done it, and I'd had a great time. If I wrap myself in cotton wool, I thought, I might as well be dead.

After the thaw in late February I went back to Jill in Birmingham. As usual I felt so much better after her treatments, but I was beginning to get depressed that even they didn't last. I sat down and thought and thought and thought. I'd been fantastically good at writing my pain diary but lousy at reading it. So I read it. All three and a half years of it.

The one thing that seemed to me to stand out was the problem with my sacroiliac joint and pelvis. Every time my SIJ had been adjusted or corrected I felt greatly improved. My pelvis felt firmer, my back pain improved, my legs seemed stronger and the muscle spasms and leg pain seemed to decrease. I had had twenty-six chiropractic appointments. Twenty-six times my SIJ had been put back in place by Meg or Danielle and a good few more times by Angela as well. Clearly these methods didn't last – for me. So was there anything that could be done about this blasted SIJ, which would keep it in place permanently and stop its propensity to slip up? This was the twenty-first century after all – surely there was something somebody could do?

As if to draw my attention to it further, if that were needed, it slipped out again, after a gardening episode in late February. I tried everything I could think of to help myself – every back exercise I'd ever done, every stretch, even hanging from the door frame, but it was no good. It was with a sense of weary inevitability that I booked an appointment with Angela. But before going I read everything I could find about SIJs, and at last I struck gold.

I read about a treatment called prolotherapy, which is an injection treatment to strengthen weakened ligaments and is used most commonly to treat low back pain. Weakened ligaments! Isn't that what Danielle had said I probably had? What exactly were ligaments? I honestly didn't know – I told you I was a complete ignoramus. Finally I got around to looking them up. A ligament is a strong band of connective tissue which connects bone to bone to form a joint. In other words it holds the joints in place. My interest was aroused and I read on. What's more, although I read plenty of American websites, I also found that this treatment was available in this country. One British article described the treatment as a "secret" cure for back pain. Why was it secret? Another said that the solutions used in the injections could be thought of as acting like a "superglue" repair to the fibro-osseous junction – the bit where ligaments attach to bones. This was what I needed – a dose of Araldite to stick me back together.

Armed with print-outs about my new discovery I took myself off to Angela. As usual I felt better straight away after her treatment. She said the good news was that my SIJ hasn't slipped up as much as last time – only half an inch. This sounded quite a lot to me – *you mean it had been worse than that before?* She still thought that I could manage the problem with core exercises and regular massage and myofascial release to keep my muscles as supple as possible, because it was tight muscles that pulled the joint up. But perhaps it was weak joints that caused the muscles to tighten up in the first place, so it was a bit of a chicken and egg situation.

I pointed out that she and Danielle had now adjusted my SIJ over thirty times between them. *Thirty!* Did she know about a treatment called prolotherapy? I gave her my print-outs on it. She looked at them and said something to the effect that she didn't think it would be harmful and it might be worthwhile but "I wouldn't want anyone doing that to my back." I knew that she too suffered from a bad back, which she'd had for many more years that I had. But she was not in pain all the time, and I was. I simply wasn't managing my problems with so-called "conservative" methods. Not only was my pain constant I had anxiety that with every move I made, even quite modest ones, I would upset my sacroiliac joint yet again. I decided I would go away and do everything she said to try to manage things with exercises. But it would be the last time. If my SIJ came out again I would think really seriously about pursuing this new discovery – prolotherapy.

As usual I paced up both my exercises and my walking. I tried thinking really hard about my core muscles and my posture. I found that if I chanted "Core and Posture" to myself it took on a march-like rhythm, eminently suitable to accompany walking. (It fits well to the tune of "Frere Jacques.")

But things were not good. Somehow I felt that this time

Angela's treatment hadn't been as successful. I couldn't say my sacroiliac joint was out exactly; just that my whole pelvis never really felt very firm. I found a helpful American internet site devoted solely to the SIJ – "www.sidysfunction.com." The authors were selling a book to go with it. I read the contents of the site several times and ordered the book, which meant phoning America direct, since it was not available on Amazon. From this book I learned about the Straight Leg Test. Quite simply you lie on your back and slowly raise each leg in turn. My left leg was easy enough to do, but my right leg – the bad one – was almost impossible to raise. It was like trying to shift concrete. Clearly my right sacroiliac joint and its associated musculature were very weak. I tried some of the recommended DIY ways of putting in my own SIJ and temporarily made things worse. The final chapter of the book recommended prolotherapy if conservative treatments had failed, thus endorsing the way my own thinking was going. I'd been trying conservative treatments for three and a half, going on four years now. Was that long enough to prove they'd failed?

My morale was raised briefly in early April at a gathering of old school friends in Shropshire, a follow-up to the great day we'd had when meeting up at the school the previous May. For a whole weekend we ate, drank, walked, played and sang music, and talked and talked and talked and talked and talked. The weather was good and we drove out to Carding Mill Valley where the fit people (the majority) walked over the Long Mynd and the unfit (myself and two others) struggled round antique shops and drank coffee in Church Stretton. I was trying not to bore everyone with my problems but inevitably some of it came out. I mentioned this new treatment I was hoping to try. "Oh you must," said one of my friends, her own activity curtailed by a dodgy knee, "you've only got one life." I knew that – it was why I'd been trying every treatment under the sun for three and a half years.

A week later Ed and I went to East Anglia for a family celebration and holiday. My elder brother's seventieth birthday party found me struggling against back pain to raise a smile, on an otherwise very happy day. We spent the next few days catching up with old friends, going on the Broads and walking. But now walking was a real struggle. My back hurt, my pelvis felt weak and unstable, and my thighs were tight and excruciatingly painful. Whatever was the matter with them? The legs which had carried me hundreds of feet into the Alps last year now couldn't seem to take me half a mile across the flattest counties of England.

When I got home I found all the trigger points and tight places in them and massaged them both manually and with the ball against the wall. It was hard and painful work. But I didn't want to spend money on more treatments which would make me feel better for a bit, but wouldn't last. I wanted the underlying *cause* of my pain addressed, and this I was sure was to do with my pelvis.

I did more research on prolotherapy. I came across a long spiel by a ski instructor who'd flown from Spain to London for this treatment and cured his back pain and naturally was an enthusiastic ambassador for it. This encouraged me more. I searched for practitioners and found the website of the British Institute of Musculoskeletal Medicine (BIMM). I didn't know there was such a thing but it sounded a reputable body. They published a list of doctors who practised prolotherapy. Most of them were working in hospitals in large cities – London, Birmingham, Bristol, Coventry. This would mean convincing my GP to give me a referral, and that might be tricky. Then there'd be a long wait, a trek to an unfamiliar location and a struggle to find my way around, let alone park. All very stressful.

Then I saw that there was actually somebody working in my own county, just over twenty miles away. Dr Pearson seemed to be working privately in his own clinic. It would mean a comfortable drive and I could refer myself, as I'd got used to doing with all my other practitioners. He had no website and I was unable to find out anything about him other than that he was a medical osteopath – a speciality I didn't know existed. I'd fought shy of private medicine until now – I was in awe of private doctors and then of course there was the expense. But I'd have to go down this road if I wanted prolotherapy. It couldn't hurt to give Dr Pearson a ring, surely. I took a deep breath and dialled the number. It was the best decision I ever made.

CHAPTER 13

Answers at Last

Diagnosis and Prolotherapy

Not surprisingly it was a secretary who answered the phone. With some trepidation I gave her my name and then said something like "I haven't been referred or anything but I'm trying to find out about prolotherapy because…"

"Before you go any further," she interrupted, "You need to talk to Dr Pearson. He happens to be free at the moment – I'll just check if he can talk to you." A few seconds later a male voice said "Well that was good timing – what can I do for you?"

I'd made notes and pretty well got a long story down to manageable size, but inevitably I had to start with doing the splits over a stile. "We're not meant to do the splits once we're out of nappies," he said. This made me smile, which helped me to relax and I continued my story a little more confidently. Soon he was asking a lot of extremely pertinent questions, which helped me to feel I might have got the right man. I managed to ask some questions of my own, the main one of which was how long he'd been doing prolotherapy. The answer was thirty years. That was the reassurance I needed and I booked an hour's appointment, during which, he said, he would take a full history, examine me and give me prolotherapy treatment, if he deemed it the right thing to do, all in one session.

I asked whether I'd be able to drive after the prolotherapy, mindful that some websites had said practitioners give gas and air while injecting, to help with pain relief. "You'll be able to drive," he answered. "You may feel as if you've been kicked in the bum, but it shouldn't stop you driving." I smiled again – I was going to get on with this guy.

A fortnight later I turned up at the appointed time. Dr Pearson was a bearded man in his early sixties. He showed me into his consulting room and asked me to tell him my story again.

"I know we spoke on the phone, but I can't remember it all, so start again from the beginning."

"Actually I've written it down. Shall I give you my notes, or would you prefer me to talk – I do tend to waffle."

"It doesn't matter. Things can come out in the waffle."

So I talked, or waffled and he made his own notes, whilst sipping tea from a mug bearing the slogan "Veni, Vidi, Vici." I smiled again, inwardly this time. Could this man really be the one to conquer? I told him again about the stile, about the groin pain, physio, chiropractic, about pubic symphysis dysfunction and sacroiliac joint dysfunction and I'd got as far as Dr Davidson and the cortisone injection into the hip when he said "Stop right there. Tell me how you felt after that injection? Did it make you feel better?" Did it? It was three years ago, and I was so unprepared for this, forgetting about Danielle's concerns and thinking that everything was down to my pelvis, that I couldn't really remember. I floundered for a bit and he fixed me with his eyes and said, "You see, it's absolutely crucial."

"It did help," I replied cautiously, thinking back. "Not immediately, but I do remember feeling better after a few days. It was much easier to put my socks on and to get in and out of the car." He made some more notes and said "OK – carry on." So I did, telling him about tight muscles, trigger points, Rolfing, myofascial release and Pilates, and how I'd put my SIJ out again after my sessions with Marion and how it kept coming out and how I'd come to the end of the road with the treatments I'd had for it and I wanted a new approach.

"All right," he said, "Let me take a look at you." So I stood up and bent forwards and backwards and to the left side and the right side and stood on one leg and then the other, which for some reason seemed to be difficult that day. Then he put his hands on my shoulders and pressed down and I sort of partially collapsed. He said, "I thought you were joking when you said Pilates stretches sent your SIJ out – but now I think I believe you." What was that supposed to mean?

I then got on the treatment table and he palpated my pelvis a bit more and then started moving my hip about. Did it hurt when he moved it close to my chest, he asked. Well yes it did a bit – in my groin. And when he moved it out to the side? Well yes, again. I knew this, but because I had so many other pains – lower back, sacroiliac joint, pubic symphysis, tight thigh muscles – I'd more or less ignored this groin pain which was nothing like as bad as it had been after the original injury.

He gave me a blanket to cover myself and took a step back and looked thoughtful. He said that the whole of what he called my pelvic ring was unstable, involving both sacroiliac joints and my pubic symphysis. In addition, my iliolumbar ligaments which join the sacrum to the spine were weak – in other words the guy ropes that hold the tent-pole in place, to return to the analogy Charlotte had given me two years previously. He thought I was slightly hypermobile, meaning I tended towards having ligament laxity in any case. The spine itself showed a mild scoliosis – a slight curve. He was prepared to give me prolotherapy into all the necessary ligaments and thought there was a good chance this would improve things.

Most of that I more or less knew or had guessed at, but now came something really unexpected. He thought I had a labral tear – *a what?* – in my hip and he wanted to refer me to a hip specialist in Coventry. I looked blank and he explained that a labral tear was a tear in the cartilage surrounding the hip joint and that it was easy to miss because it didn't show up on normal X-rays or scans. The only way to see it was to inject a dye into the hip joint and then do a scan – a procedure known as an MRI arthrogram. If a tear was found it could then be tidied up with a hip arthroscopy – keyhole surgery. Was I prepared to go to see someone called Professor Green in Coventry privately? It took me all of thirty seconds to say yes. This was going to cost serious money now, but I didn't care because it seemed as if this might be a significant breakthrough.

After a few moments to let me take it all in he said gently, "I can't see that you've got much choice really." Except to carry on as I am, I thought, with chronic pain and reduced function, repeating treatments that only work temporarily, spending a fortune and getting more depressed and more frustrated with each month that passed. It was a no-brainer really.

He said all the people I'd seen till now had looked at things from their own training, and it would have been better if I'd seen a sports physician who would have had much more of a multi-disciplinary approach to injuries such as mine.

"I didn't know there were such people."

"No, most people don't."

At least two of the clinics I'd attended had claimed to treat sports injuries, and Christine was a sports physiotherapist, and I'd thought that was good enough, although I had sometimes wondered who treated the Beckhams of this world. If only Dr Davidson had thought to say something along these lines when he first told me I had a sports injury!

I realised that my hour was nearly up and although he said he could "prolo in seven minutes" I must have looked slightly shocked because he then said it might be better if I went away, thought everything over and came back in a week's time for the first of three prolotherapy treatments into my pelvic ligaments. In the meantime he would write a letter of referral to Professor Green as well as one to my GP about all that we'd discussed.

I told him that I'd had conflicting statements about pelvises which I'd found confusing and had even been told on one occasion that sacroiliac joints can't move. At this he flung his arms out in frustration and said, "Then why did God put them there?" SIJs move very slightly, he said, to act as shock absorbers when we walk. Unless of course you're injured like me, when they move too much. I *knew* mine moved too much, especially the right one, which even now was not in place. I got dressed, paid, made an appointment for prolotherapy treatment for the following week and left.

I sat in the car and wept. Mostly it was relief that I had finally, finally, finally after nearly four years, got what seemed now to be a definitive diagnosis. And relief that it wasn't my fault, as I sometimes thought it was, for occasionally slacking off with my exercises or not paying 100% attention to my posture. There were real things wrong with me, which neither exercises nor correct posture alone would fix. But there was shock too – shock at this additional, totally unexpected diagnosis of a problem with my hip, which had obviously not been fixed by cortisone. Partly also it was anger, though directed at no-one in particular, that it had taken this long. Mixed in there was also fear and anxiety at the long road still ahead, yet another new person to meet – a Professor no less – with possible surgery at the end of it all.

But at least there was a road ahead. A clear, signposted road, instead of the impenetrable fog I'd been stuck in for four years, trying out this treatment and that therapy, sticking a pin in and hoping for the best. And I'd been right to keep going with my quest for answers and not give up looking as I'd been told to do at Pain Management. I felt vindicated. I started the engine and drove home, arriving to dust everywhere and the sounds of hammers and drills as builders knocked down a wall in our kitchen. We were having major house works done and I hadn't picked the best moment to arrive home in such a fragile condition!

I'd got my answers, and I didn't like them. I was in no doubt whatever that Dr Pearson was right – everything he'd said fitted with how I experienced my body. If my pelvis and lumbar spine were unstable it explained why my muscles and fascia kept tightening. Even stabilising muscles could only stabilise so much if the joints were moving too much – it was like pitching your tent on quicksand. And if there was a problem with my hip too that explained my groin pain – which was *not* "referring" from something else – and why my psoas muscle kept tightening. The basic underlying cause was mechanical and the myofascial pain was secondary to that. Myofascial release therefore, which had seemed such a wonder treatment the previous year, could only ever be a temporary fix unless something was done to address the underlying problems and restore stability where it was needed.

Dr Pearson had one last little revelation up his sleeve. I was to see rather a lot of him in the coming weeks and months and I'm not exactly sure when he told me that he suspected I had a slippage of a vertebra, but eventually I understood that this was part of the mix as well. L4, he thought, had slipped forward on L5 making a "step," which was creating further instability in my back – a condition known as spondylolisthesis (which he can say and I can't). This presumably was causing the excessive "lordosis", or curve in my lower back, which both Christine and Marion had tried to cure by giving me wall-flattening exercises. He could try and fix that with prolotherapy too, by injecting into the intra-spinal ligaments. Great! Where would it all end? No wonder I was in pain with all this going on.

It only remained for the suspected labral tear to be confirmed and then I'd have the complete diagnosis – the answers to the question I'd spent four years asking: "What is wrong with me?" For that I would need to wait a little longer yet.

"You came back," he quipped as I entered the reception area a week later. I smiled weakly. I'd had to psych myself up all over again for this visit and might well not have done – perhaps he guessed this? Once in the consulting room he then asked if I had any questions from the previous week, given that it had been "rather unusual." Oh, I was so fed up with being unusual! I couldn't think of any questions apart from ones about prolotherapy itself and those were very vague. Dr Pearson was convinced that my hip was a significant cause of my problems and that it needed fixing, but thought it was worth a go to try and "stick the pelvis together" first. Then when I had "two good hips holding me up" I could have further prolotherapy injections into my iliolumbar ligaments and anything else that needed it. That he thought was the clinically sound way to proceed, so that is what, over the next few months, happened.

My sacroiliac joint was out – it had probably been so for several weeks. Dr Pearson's way of re-aligning it was to grasp me from behind, then sort of jerk me upwards in one very swift manoeuvre. I'd never had anything remotely like this before – was this what they call a high velocity thrust? I couldn't tell whether it had done the trick in realigning my SIJ or not.

Now for the prolo. I got on the treatment table and waited for the needles. He was to use a solution of dextrose with some local anaesthetic mixed in. Prolotherapy has a reputation for being painful and although I was used to painful procedures by now I couldn't help being apprehensive. Whether it was Dr Pearson's skill, his reassuring patter, the local anaesthetic or a combination of all three, it wasn't nearly as bad as I feared. He injected each pelvic joint in turn and I practised my visualisation technique "seeing" mental images of the Cornish coast and it didn't last long.

I felt much more positive as I left this time. I'd had the treatment and it had been nothing like as bad as I'd expected. It had been way below Rolfing and ITB acupuncture on my personal Painometer of procedures and I knew I needn't dread the subsequent sessions anything like so much. I drove home, if not exactly singing not crying either, and with something like hope in my heart.

Prolotherapy is not new. The principle behind it dates back to ancient Greece when historians recorded that Hippocrates treated the injured shoulders of javelin throwers with hot lances to create small amounts of scar tissue around the shoulder joint. Modern methods are rather less draconian. An American, Dr George Hackett, was the first to use injections and he also coined the name because the technique promotes "proliferation" of new cells. The solution injected creates an inflammatory response, which is the body's normal way of repairing itself. The localized inflammation – sore at first – triggers a wound-healing cascade, resulting in the laying down of new collagen, the building material of ligaments. New collagen shrinks as it matures, tightening the ligament that was injected and making it stronger. Because the body itself is doing the healing it is described as a natural process, though sticking a three-inch needle into someone doesn't sound very natural to me.

It is not a quick fix. Usually several sessions of treatment are given – Dr Pearson gave his in sets of three – and the body then starts the gradual healing process, which can take up to two or three months. For various reasons it has not become fully accepted by the medical profession, although it has to be given by doctors. Once I started to research it I found plenty of websites devoted to it, claiming its benefits. It stimulates the body to do its own repair, whereas commonly prescribed anti-inflammatory medications and cortisone injections may actually often hinder the healing process.

My second session was not to be for three weeks and in between I tried to monitor how I felt. The soreness from the injections wore off after two or three days. I had backache on and off, nothing new there. Then my groin began to hurt and my hip began catching as I walked, as if it was saying, "Yes, I'm really the problem." But as usual every day was different, and some days were not too bad at all. And I managed a decent amount of walking over the half-term holiday when for once the weather was fine, culminating in ascending to the top of the Malvern Hills. Aided by my trusty corset and walking poles, I'd achieved something I'd wanted to do for years and felt elated as I stood on Worcestershire Beacon gazing across the Severn Valley and over to the Cotswolds.

I approached my second prolotherapy session in early June with less trepidation than the first, but also with less hope, as I hadn't felt any improvement. Dr Pearson surprised me by saying, "you won't." I looked astonished and he said I wasn't likely to notice much difference till about six to eight weeks after the third injection. I hadn't taken in the time-scale of the treatment, which is quite long, because ligaments grow very slowly. Eight weeks from now would be August 1st – my nephew's wedding day. Maybe I'd have two things to celebrate then.

He told me he'd only met three people in thirty years for whom he'd had to fix the whole pelvic ring. So it seemed I really was quite an "unusual" – maybe even a rare – case. I had the next set of prolotherapy injections – which seemed if anything less painful than the first – booked the next appointment and went home. The process was repeated a fortnight later, by which time I'd had a date for a half day of hip investigations in Coventry. Dr Pearson performed his "veterinary work," as he called it on my pelvic ligaments, and we parted company for the time being with the agreement that I would ring him when I had further news about my hip and that we would take it from there. Once again life was about to take a new direction.

CHAPTER 14

Hip, Hip Hooray!

Surgery

When I typed "hip labral tear" or "hip arthroscopy" into Google I came up with plenty of relevant hits. When, however I typed in "hip pain" I found lots of information on osteoarthritis and other conditions such as Perthes Disease but not a single reference to labral tears. In other words I had to know what was wrong with me before I could find out what was wrong with me, which was a bit of a Catch-22 situation.

As I read up about labral tears I found a common theme. It seems they are more common than had been hitherto thought and that they are often overlooked or misdiagnosed as – guess what – groin strains! How many other people are out there, I wondered, with a misdiagnosis for groin pain?

I felt a Charlie that I had ignored my hip as a possible cause of some of my problems. The clues had been there. Dr Davidson had injected it because he'd suspected "irritation," Mr Lindsey had needled the surrounding musculature for a "disordered" hip, Danielle had suspected hip problems. And what about all those times I'd had to cross one leg over the other and found it searingly painful? And those exercises I'd tried from the internet? How would it all have turned out if I'd gone to see the physio Danielle recommended?

But should I really blame myself? I wasn't a professional after all. Not everybody by any means had considered my hip as a problem whereas virtually *everybody* I'd seen was in agreement that I had a sacroiliac joint problem. I'd also read, indeed been told, that groin pain can be "referred" pain from the SIJ. So that was what I thought it was. What really made things difficult was that there were several things wrong and it seemed to me that all the pains got a bit mixed up. The whole pelvic/hip/lower back area is extremely complicated and many things can go wrong there, either singly or in combination. I didn't blame anybody for missing it – I just felt extremely grateful to Dr Pearson for suspecting a hip problem and for knowing where to refer me.

On July 3rd Ed and I went to Coventry for my hip investigations. I had a CT scan, an ordinary X-ray, the injection of dye under another X-ray, and an MRI scan, one after the other. Then I had an assessment with a male physio, which included all the movements and tests I'd now become so used to. Did I have any pain he asked? Not a lot really – just a feeling of discomfort when my hip was abducted or flexed across my body. I had a momentary fear. Suppose I didn't have anything wrong with my hip? Suppose they found nothing? Suddenly I desperately wanted something to be wrong in order that I could get the answers Dr. Pearson had led me to expect. "D'you think I've got a hip problem," I asked, dreading he'd say no. "I do think you've got a hip problem," he replied. "I can detect femoral acetabular impingement – FAI." *What?* I looked blank, as well I might, and he said, "Don't worry,

Professor Green will have all the results and will talk you through it all again."

Femoral acetabular impingement, I decided, as I crunched an apple – a hastily grabbed lunch – must be a fancy name for the catching feeling I sometimes had in my hip, and the feeling that it was about to give way.

The appointment with Professor Green was the last of the day. He courteously invited Ed and me into his consulting room. He told me he'd read the very detailed letter from Dr Pearson, and seemed impressed with it. He asked me about my pain and I found myself saying all the wrong things, talking about my back and my sacroiliac joint, perhaps through nerves at meeting this eminent man. "I deal with hips," he said, "all day and every day." I wanted to rewind the session and start again.

But then things started to go better. Could I jump on the treatment table, he asked so that he could do his own assessment? I said I could get onto it, but jump – no. He laughed and said "That's part of the test," at which Ed and I also laughed and I finally started to relax. He moved my hip about, not a great deal I thought, but by now he had all the evidence he needed and I think he'd already made up his mind.

On his computer screens were all the images from the tests I'd had earlier. First he showed us the X-ray. He astonished me by asking if I'd had any problems with my hips as a child, because my sockets were rather shallow. I'd spent most of my childhood climbing trees, riding bikes and horses and romping with dogs. Clearly, no.

The CT scan which showed my hips and surrounding

tissues looking like joints of meat from the butchers was to show bone density and mine was good, Professor Green said. I'm glad something was. Finally we went back to the first screen where he changed the image from the X-ray to the MRI scan, rotated it, enlarged it and then drew our attention to what looked like a hairline crack. That was it – the tear, running raggedly through the cartilage in the labrum. Ed was impressed with the sophisticated images and the way they were being manipulated on the screen; I was just sitting there thinking "he's found it, he's found the tear!"

Professor Green said he was prepared to do a hip arthroscopy, but that I must be aware that it would only help my groin pain, not everything else. I could see he was being very careful not to raise my expectations. But it had to be a step in the right direction surely? The hip would be put into traction while the surgery was done and afterwards there would be plenty of post-operative physio, both in the hospital and back at home.

"Can I have that with my physio in Cheltenham?" I asked
"Yes."
"Am I likely to get arthritis in my hip in years to come?"
"Yes."
So that was a joy to look forward to. But hopefully for now this arthroscopy would buy me some time. "It might buy you quite a lot of time," Dr Pearson was to say later. Surgery was booked in for September 15th.

A few days later I rang Dr Pearson to let him know that he was vindicated in his diagnosis and that Professor Green had decided to go ahead with surgery. Dr. Pearson said that he thought my hip was "a significant contributory factor" to my problems and that I wasn't that old (*good*) and that he'd be disappointed if he couldn't improve things for me after I'd had the operation.

Even so as the summer wore on it was not my hip but my back that gave me the most grief. It was my back that hurt throughout my nephew's wedding, our holiday in Guernsey and Swanage and right up to the day of the surgery. I couldn't say I felt any improvement from the prolotherapy and was sure that the strong pain I was feeling could only be caused by a misaligned SIJ. However, there was still a lot more treatment in the pipeline so I gritted my teeth and forced myself to be positive as we walked some of Guernsey's beautiful coastal paths. I even swam – gently – in the hotel pool and in the sea at Swanage, where we hit an unexpected three days of beautiful weather.

In late August a letter arrived from Coventry – a follow-up to my day of investigations. Professor Green was going to do a debridement on my hip, it said, which meant smoothing down the surfaces of the torn cartilage, not something that used to happen to girls on their wedding night.

Ed and I arrived early at the hospital as requested on 15th September and Professor Griffin appeared and marked up my right leg with a black marker pen. Well, you never know! I was last on the operating list and was taken up to theatre at around one o'clock. I was moved from my bed to an incredibly uncomfortable operating trolley. My hip didn't hurt at all but my back was killing me. With the anaesthetic already starting to work, all I could think of was "my back, oh God, my back – are they really operating on the right bit?" – and then I went under.

We often take for granted the wonders of modern medicine. You go to sleep and then you wake up and (in most cases) get better. Meanwhile incredibly skilled people have opened up your body, done amazing things inside, sewn it up again, whilst keeping you alive but pain-free, and written it all up whilst you, the patient, are blissfully unaware. If it is keyhole surgery as mine was you even get pretty pictures of it all. Also you only have the tiniest of scars and your recovery time is much quicker.

I was wakened by one of the theatre staff to hear the wonderful words, "Wake up, Liz. It's all over and it went well." I was glad to hear that because I felt lousy, a feeling which worsened as I was wheeled back to my room, where Ed was so patiently waiting. It seemed no time at all before Professor Green was there, telling me what he'd done. He'd smoothed down the tear, he said, and removed three loose bodies of cartilage as well as a piece of very inflamed tissue called a ligamentum teres, which he thought might have been significant in causing my pain. I remembered to thank him before shutting my eyes and giving in to wooziness, caused by low blood pressure. I'd been pumped full of pain killers and was vaguely aware of one wonderful thing – I had no back-pain. However, my leg felt as if it had been pulled out of its socket. Which, in fact, it had been – partially anyway.

Gradually I improved and took sips of water and even struggled to eat the sandwiches I was later given. Ed, who had waited around all day, went off to have some supper before saying goodbye and leaving to drive home about 7pm. Soon after, I took my first steps with crutches to the loo. Although I'd been told I could be fully weight-bearing I couldn't help but be very cautious. It was fine! Walking didn't hurt! I'd been prepared for there to be at least some pain in the joint but there was none. Mind you, I was stuffed to the eyeballs with painkillers.

I was fixed up with a strange device on my leg called a cryo cuff, which looked like a cross between a shower mat and an octopus. It had tubes attached to a container of cold water which was continuously pumped into it, thus keeping my leg and hip joint cool. In addition a physio came in and fixed me up for an hour with another machine which moved my leg backwards and forwards to keep everything as supple as possible, in what is known as Continuous Passive Motion. Thus attired I dozed in front of the telly all evening and went to sleep properly after my evening medication at around 10pm.

I was woken at 6.30am by a nurse who took my blood pressure which was very low, and my temperature which wasn't, and gave me my pills to take when breakfast came. I lay there slowly surfacing and was conscious of two delicious things. The first was that I'd had the best night's sleep of my life, helped no doubt by all the medication. The second was that I had no pain anywhere. None at all. I lay there luxuriating in this state. How long, I wondered, was I going to be allowed to stay in this blissful condition?

The answer was all of half a morning. I ate a hearty breakfast after my near starvation the previous day. I then got up with the aid of my crutches and moved around – yes, my leg was still there, and yes it didn't hurt. I showered and dressed and waited for one of the physios to come and collect me, as she'd said she would.

There were four of us being taken to physio, all women – Professor Green's "list" of the previous day. We limped in a crutch-clutching convoy down the corridor, into a lift, along another shorter corridor and into a gym. Two of us got onto exercise bikes, whilst the other two lay on treatment tables and did various exercises including bum squeezes to strengthen our gluteals. Ah, bum squeezes! I knew all about those! After ten minutes we swapped round.

In the afternoon we repeated the session; although this time we didn't use the lift but were taught how to go up and down the stairs. Good leg first for going up, bad leg first for coming down – "up to heaven and down to hell". It took a bit of time, especially as one patient's idea of the ideal footwear for climbing stairs the day after hip surgery was flip-flops.

That was the end of my pain-free status. I felt very sore after the morning session and even more so after the afternoon session, despite gulping down all the pain-killers I was being given at frequent intervals. I lay on my bed unable to move my leg at all without pain, and wondering if it had all been a dreadful mistake. The physios linked me up again to the cryo cuff and the leg-waggling machine and the pain began to ease. I spent the rest of the day reading and watching telly and had a look at the operation notes and the photos of the inside of my hip. Amazing! I wondered if the cartilage tear might have behaved a bit like a torn fingernail and the loose bodies like some stones in one's shoe. Maybe I'd been constantly subconsciously adjusting my walking to get away from these irritants. Hopefully this would all change now.

After another good night's sleep I went for my final physio session. I still had groin pain but this time the bike work seemed to ease it rather than increase it and my spirits were raised. I resolved to dig out the very basic, third-hand exercise bike I had lurking at the back of the garage when I got home. One of the physios said maybe the previous day's sessions had been a bit much for me as I was the only one who'd not been up and about on the day of the surgery. That made me feel better. It also came out in conversation with her that I'd had hip pain for four years. "We get quite a lot of people who've been round the houses not getting the right treatment," she said. This only served to emphasise that labral tears are more common than previously thought.

By lunchtime I was all packed and ready and my spirits had soared. Ed arrived to fetch me. Carefully crutching my way along the corridors I thanked the nurses, said my goodbyes and made for the lift. I was going home.

There followed ten weeks of rehab monitored by Angela. I'd not seen her for six months and greeted her as an old friend. To start with things went well. I phased out the medication and was off crutches before too long. I did all my exercises religiously and practised my bum squeezes so diligently and so focused on them one morning in the kitchen that I burnt the toast. I used the old exercise bike I'd inherited until it began to smell hot and shed fine black powder on the floor. I worked and worked at it all and felt strength building up in my hip and thigh muscles week by week. I also paced up my walking. At the end of September I was doing only five minute walks, by the middle of October it was half a mile, by the end of that month a whole mile and by the end of November I was managing nearly two miles. I felt really heartened by this achievement. I'd be rambling again in 2010!

So my hip was getting better, but what about my back – my wretched, wretched back? It wasn't getting better, it was if anything getting worse. I drew the obvious conclusion – my right SIJ must have slipped up again. Yes of course it had. In fact I was pretty sure it had been out for several months, which made me depressed, thinking that the prolotherapy I'd had couldn't have been very successful. Angela corrected it again with her Muscle Energy Technique and as always I felt better straight away. I couldn't know it at the time, but that was to be the last time she would do it.

I didn't feel ready to go back to Dr Pearson for any more injections just yet. But I did ring him up. He was pleased with all the good news about the hip, and said although it was disappointing that my back was bad, not to despair. He thought prolotherapy injections were more likely to be effective now that my hip had been repaired – exactly what I'd been hoping he'd say. I said I'd contact him again when I felt up to having more sessions of it.

Phase two and three exercises of my hip rehab proved harder precisely because of my back. Together Angela and I selected the ones that I could do which were sufficient for my needs. I wasn't an elite athlete, as most of Professor Green's patients were. All I wanted to do was walk.

Also on the rehab agenda were water-based exercises so I started going to the local pool, now beautifully refurbished after the 2007 floods. The rehab notes suggested that you "walk in chest deep water," so I went into the baby pool and waded back and forth among the parents and curious toddlers. I felt a total prat and couldn't face doing it again. So for my other sessions I remained in the main pool, and holding onto the concrete surround at the shallow end, did "flutter kicks" – another recommended exercise. "You're not getting very far," said a friendly lady, just completing some lengths. So I explained and found to my surprise that she seemed quite interested in my story. Gradually I incorporated a few lengths of crawl too – breast stroke was still out – but as autumn became winter and my back started getting worse again my enthusiasm for swimming, never very great at the best of times, waned and I stopped going.

Six weeks after my surgery, after we'd been let down by a decorator, I donned my lumbar corset and helped Ed decorate the dining room and conservatory. We'd survived the noise of drills and hammers, piles of rubble and weeks of dust as builders and fitters had altered our dining area, built a conservatory and installed a new kitchen. Although the main building work was finished we could not get the laminated flooring down or the curtains up till the decorating was done. I don't think I did myself any harm and the psychological lift from seeing what had been a long project nearing fruition was worth it. I was up and down with various pains for most of the following month, but mostly due to my back, not my hip. When Angela signed me off on 20th November I passed all my hip tests with flying colours and she was able to fax through a very positive report to Professor Green's team. If only it was as simple to sort out my back!

In early December, nearly three months after my hip surgery I went back to Dr Pearson. He thought there was some improvement in my pelvic joints, though I was very unsure, given that Angela had only recently had to realign my right SIJ. He decided to concentrate on the iliolumbar ligaments. But in addition to sticking L4 and L5 to the ilium – lashing the guy ropes to the tent pole – he wanted to inject the intra-spinal ligaments to see what he could do about stabilising the spine where L4 had slipped forward on L5 – the spondylolisthesis. How long had I had this I wondered?

Months, years? Was it relatively new? No-one else had mentioned it. It didn't occur to me at this point that Angela's description of my L4 being "jammed in" might refer to the same thing. Had I caused it, or made it worse doing McKenzie back exercises? It was pointless to speculate, better just to let him get on with it.

So I had my injections and there seemed to be quite a lot of them, although I couldn't really tell what was going on. He said if it was any consolation his own back was very bad and he'd got a whole lot of treatment lined up for it, starting with prolotherapy the following day. I said, "It's no consolation – I don't want other people to suffer, just because I do." I was really sore after these injections and on the way home stiffened up so much I could hardly get out of the car. But it wore off after a day, and the second set two weeks later didn't feel too bad at all. Dr Pearson reassured me that spondylolisthesis was not so terrible; many people had it without any symptoms and without even knowing they'd got it.

We had a party and family celebrations for Ed's birthday – one of those Significant Birthdays – and an early Christmas on the 17th and 18th December, which left us free for Christmas itself. We'd decided to treat ourselves to a festive break at a hotel in Deddington, Oxfordshire. Here we ate wonderful food and were warm and cosy, something we weren't at home. Our boiler had broken down, just as the family – and the snow – had arrived the previous weekend. We'd now spent a week running around from one room to another with electric heaters, and boiling kettles for hot water as the temperature plummeted to near record levels, and we were getting fed up with it.

One of the first things I did at the hotel was to fill the bath and have a hot soak, feeling the warmth penetrate right to my bones. My back had felt firmer by the day since the two recent prolotherapy treatments and I suddenly found myself in the bath sitting up and lying down and sitting up and lying down just because I could. So that was what it was like to have a strong back! I didn't remember it feeling like this for months, actually for years. Oh wonderful prolotherapy! Was my back fixed as well as my hip had been? Was this the beginning of the end?

On Boxing Day Ed and I undertook a 5-mile circular route round the village, which I completed with no problems at all. Yes, I really would be rambling in the New Year!

Refreshed from our break we returned to our cold house. It was to be nearly three weeks before we managed to fix the boiler, during which we had snow and night-time temperatures of -8. But I felt good! Nothing could dampen my spirits. On New Year's Eve, three months after my hip operation, I danced the night away at the local barn dance. One of the friends we'd made there the previous year said most warmly and touchingly, "It's so good to see you dancing and joining in". The following day I climbed to the top of Cleeve Hill on the annual New Year's Day walk, something I'd been forced to forego the previous year. Both activities left me a bit sore, but it wore off before too long. I was elated. I'd got my life back! I could do all of the things I wanted to do.

I had one more prolotherapy session to go. My back was feeling great so one more would be the icing on the cake, I thought. I bounced into Dr Pearson's surgery on January 4th, bearing a bottle of wine and overflowing with gratitude, telling him that I'd been dancing and climbing hills and that he'd turned my life around. I had my injections and thanked him profusely as I left. He said, "Don't take this the wrong way, but I hope I'll never see you again". Despite my new-found confidence I must have looked a bit uncertain, because he then said, "Don't think if you want to come back that it's been a failure". With this reassurance I thanked him again and left. I was bursting with pent-up energy to get on with my life. I was already looking forward to the spring, planning the walks I'd do, the plants to buy for the garden – living life to the full and behaving like a normal person.

Little did I know that in two months I'd be back again in his surgery and that living a full life and being pain free would go back on hold for a long, long time to come.

CHAPTER 15

Back to the Drawing Board

More Prolotherapy and Myofascial Release

The Christmas snow had more or less melted but another huge swathe of it came in on January 5th 2010. It snowed and snowed and snowed. Ed cleared a good deal of it the following day, but there was still a great deal to do and I said I'd have a go. I shovelled and swept and my back began to hurt, but I kept at it. I was fine, I was invincible now, I wasn't going to be a wimp; there were loads of people in the world far worse off than me. The pain increased, so I decided OK, perhaps I really had better stop. I went and lay down and as fire began to course through my back I thought, whoops, I've done it again.

There was nothing for it but to take pain killers and sit it out. Ed got the boiler working, after a phone call to a helpful boiler repair man, by the simple expedient of squirting WD40 into the fan and eventually the snow melted, the fields became green again and life resumed some sort of normality.

The soreness had gone from my back but so too had the strength, and my SIJs – both of them – were playing up too. I couldn't think of anything else to do other than go back to Dr Pearson. His response to my shame-faced phone call telling him that I'd messed things up was one of surprise but in no way negative. This time it was back to basics, injecting the whole pelvic ring again and also the iliolumbar ligaments. I decided that if it hadn't been shovelling snow it would have been something else – I had never felt totally sure that my pelvis had been stabilised by the treatment so far.

"Pelvic stability is vital," Dr Pearson said, "It's the bedrock for supporting the upper body. It's like the ground."

"For pitching your tent on?"

"Exactly."

He didn't seem to be upset that I'd shovelled snow – he said you've got to find out what stresses your body can take. This time, however, he also said, "keep moving, but stay upright". I didn't need to be told that after this latest flare-up.

Winter dragged on, but on dry days I went for local walks and noted how strong my hip felt. By the end of February I felt a small amount of improvement in my pelvis too. We went with some friends to a pub folk singing night, which involved sitting on hard chairs for several hours. At the end of the evening everyone was complaining about their backs – except me. Mine felt fine!

I had another two prolo sessions in March to complete this particular lot of three and then was on my own again to see how things went. I often felt sore, usually from overdoing stretches. But how could I tell how much to stretch before it becomes overdoing? Nevertheless, things seemed to be moving in the right direction.

The cold winter had given way to a very wet March, but now finally spring was blossoming – and what a spring! Suddenly the birds, the flowers, the trees and the hedges were awake and firing on all cylinders – riotous birdsong, green shoots and bright flowers were suffusing the senses. April got warmer and warmer until suddenly it was the middle of the month and the weekend of my sixtieth birthday when we had a positive heat wave. Oh dear – sixty. I'd had no difficulty with forty or fifty, but sixty is different. Sixty like it or not, is the beginning of being old. Never mind sixty being the "new forty;" it can only be that if you've got excellent health and I didn't have. Sixty as far as I was concerned was sixty. Perhaps now I could begin to accept that my body was slowly running down. I know plenty of people keeping fit and active well into their seventies, even eighties – my own parents had been great examples of this. And I could certainly go on fighting, go on looking for improvements, never giving up because if you do, you might as well die. Nevertheless, as the year wore on I found I was accepting my aches and pains more, was accepting that my body was not as good, and never would be, as it had been.

You've either got to deny it or go for it and I'd decided to go for it. I invited my entire extended family to a birthday lunch and nearly all of them made it – even one nephew who moved heaven and earth to get back from Germany, where work had taken him, when the infamous Icelandic ash-cloud grounded all the planes. It was a lovely day with amazing weather and was, I think, enjoyed by all the generations – and by my brother's dog, who availed herself of our filthy muddy stream to cool down!

By the end of May I was gardening happily on hands and knees, still with back pain it's true, but without any pelvic or hip pain – in fact I'd forgotten all about my hip. I'd also stopped worrying that my SIJ was going to slip up at any moment. It had now been seven months since its last re-alignment from Angela – the longest it had stayed in place. This time I felt that the prolotherapy into my pelvic joints had really worked. I'm sure it was because my SIJ was in place and my hip function was so much better and I was properly aligned, so that at last sticking me together could be really effective. At last, at last! Finally my pelvis had been stabilised, and that was another huge step forward in my healing.

I could now tick off both my hip and my pelvis; time now to have another go with prolo on my lumbar spine and try to cure the spondylolisthesis. I remembered how good I'd felt at Christmas and felt confident that, with my pelvis now stable, a further set of three prolo injections would work well.

It was not to be. I had the three injections but at the last session Dr Pearson said he thought my spondy was worse, not better. I certainly knew that I still had pain – in my legs as well as my back – and that the strength I'd had in my back at Christmas briefly – oh, so briefly – had not returned. Nevertheless I decided to give it the three full months before contacting him again, and see if over that time things would improve.

I now knew that after prolo injections I had to take it very easy for quite a long time and I really tried hard to do just that. The soreness from the injections should have worn off by the time we drove to Scotland in late July, but it hadn't. At the last minute I put a phone number into my bag to consult in an emergency. And on the third day, as I was sitting in the car park at Dumfries waiting for Ed to return from an errand with what felt like flames shooting through my back, I decided that the emergency was now. I rang the number. It was that of Ruth

Duncan in Glasgow, the founder of the John F. Barnes method of myofascial release in the UK. It was Ruth herself who answered the phone. I introduced myself as a patient of her colleague Jill in Birmingham and asked if it was possible for her to see me as a one-off emergency when we arrived in Glasgow in a couple of days. Yes, she could fit me in on Friday morning. I was grateful. This would be a strange way of spending a holiday but I didn't care. All I wanted was relief from pain.

On the Friday morning I left Ed in a Glasgow library whilst I took the underground out of the city centre, following the instructions Ruth had given me. Despite the state of my back I was quite excited at the thought of meeting "the" Ruth Duncan, who as well as having her own treatment practice, lectured and trained others and had done so much to spread the work of John F. Barnes into this country. Within minutes of meeting me she had assessed that my back was tight and rotated, my pelvis tipped forward (though thankfully nothing was "out"), my psoas and piriformis muscles tight. She got me to position myself on a kneeler chair with my back spread-eagled across her treatment couch, so that she could really get to work on it. She massaged and stretched and kneaded and pulled and pushed to try and get some movement into my muscles which she said were solid. She knew all about prolotherapy and was concerned that with my back in such a state the injected ligaments, around my L4 and L5 vertebrae, wouldn't repair correctly. She finished the session with deep work on the psoas muscle to free up pain in my groin.

Oh the relief! I felt better straight away. It had felt like there was a war going on in my back, between the ligaments which were trying to re-grow, and the tight muscles which were pulling against them in the opposite direction. Perhaps prolotherapy was not the answer for fixing my slippage. I had read that it is most effective if the body is in correct alignment *before* treatment, and if a vertebra had slipped forward that clearly wasn't so in my case. And what about the slight scoliosis (twist in the spine) that Dr Pearson had once mentioned. That would surely cause back muscles to spasm up wouldn't it? Yet I hadn't felt the same problems at Christmas – my back had felt wonderfully aligned and strong, so clearly it had been worth a second try to fix it with prolo. Dr Pearson's rationale at the time had been not to try to undo the "step", but to stabilise the spine so that there was less movement – the wrong kind of movement.

I tried over the rest of our time in Scotland to use my body correctly, to think about core and posture, and to enjoy the rest of my holiday.

Back from Scotland with an improved back from Ruth's treatment but with very painful legs – sometimes they were very sore after just a trip to the letter-box – I decided to try sports massage. And so yet another therapist, Steve, entered my life. He was local, which was one of my reasons for choosing him, and very competent. Over four sessions he worked on all the relevant muscles with deep massage, which was painful, and acupuncture, which wasn't. Everything was super tight – AGAIN. He wanted me to stretch, but *gently*. I was always going at it hammer and tongs and then being surprised when I caused soreness.

I was *determined* to walk – what was the point in paying all that money for hip surgery but then being beaten by sore tight muscles? In mid-September we went for a mini walking break on Exmoor and the Quantocks, and within two days my legs were as painful as ever, despite my lumbar corset and despite my stretches which I did three times a day. Surely I couldn't have undone all Steve's work in such a short time? Was there something else going on? It was depressing. I *am* going to have to stop walking, I thought. Is it really worth it? Accept it, woman, whatever's going on, your legs just aren't right for serious walking any more. Develop other interests – such as playing the piano. I had been successful earlier in the year in our local festival and had got a small buzz from that, and I'd also started playing duos purely for leisure with a cellist I'd met on a ramble the previous year.

So I stopped walking, other than was necessary – for the time being anyway, and my legs were grateful. But with my back feeling bad again my mood was not good.

It was late September when, tidying up some internet bookmarks, I came across something I'd marked months, probably years, ago. It was called a back "Mobiliser". It was a mattress that you lay on with a built-in heat pad and rollers that moved up and down under you, flexing and extending the spine and massaging all the back muscles at the same time – and it was fearsomely expensive. It was endorsed not only by all sorts of famous sports people but also by the British Army who I felt would not put their name to something lightly. It was clearly the expense that had deterred me from pursuing it before. But I'd been going round in circles for five years now and my thinking was different. *If I got a Mobiliser I would be in control of my own treatment and could stop the merry-go-round of driving all over the place to endless appointments whose results didn't last. I could have my back massaged every day, which would stop*

156

it spasming up. It might well be money saved in the long run. I emailed the company with questions and got a reply. If I hired a Mobiliser for four months, I would be able to have a good taster of what it could do, and I would get support and advice from the company through an online "diary."

I mulled it over for days and days and then discovered something else. There was to be a Back Pain Show at Olympia at the end of October, just as half-term was starting. There was to be a full two-day programme of lectures and demonstrations and trade stands all devoted to backs. Surely if nothing else I would learn a great deal. And I fancied a trip to London anyway and a stay with my London friends. I ordered tickets for both days. I would go to the show and then drive to the Bristol shop which hired the Mobiliser one day the following week.

On October 4th I went back to Dr Pearson not for more needles but to update him on the last three months. I was in a lot of pain on that particular day, so it was easy to pour everything out. I felt listened to, thought about and understood – his comment about how chronic pain can wear you down was well-timed for the mood I was in. I told him about the soreness from the last lot of prolotherapy lasting a long time, about the emergency trip to Ruth Duncan, about the fact that my back was still very painful – in short that this time the prolotherapy hadn't seemed to have helped. He checked my back and found I still had the slippage.

"I'd like to try another approach," I said.

"I'm afraid there aren't many other options."

"What about gadgets?"

"Gadgets," he replied evenly, but not thank goodness

mockingly, "gadgets and gizmos".

I told him about the Mobiliser and showed him a sheet I'd downloaded, wondering if he'd be sceptical but he wasn't at all, indeed he seemed quite interested. I was beginning to understand that this man, who practised both orthodox and complementary medicine and had suffered for years with a bad back of his own, was open to all suggestions.

I spent ages talking to him about all my aches and pains, exploring all the possibilities of what was causing both the back and the leg pains, and left with his full permission for me to try the Mobiliser and anything else, provided I monitored everything. On leaving I checked my watch – I'd been there an hour and a half, but had been charged for only half an hour. I felt a huge rush of gratitude. He wants me to get better, I thought, lots of people want me to get better. I remembered that others – especially Danielle, Charlotte, and Angela – had often gone the extra mile with email and phone support. So it was with renewed heart that I went home determined yet again to see what I could do for myself.

CHAPTER 16

Gadgets and Gizmos

The Back Show and the Mobiliser

I had an accumulation of items at home purporting to relieve back pain, some of which were useful, such as the Tens machine, my lumbar corset, a Pilates mat for floor exercises and of course the crutches, and many of which weren't and which were now cluttering up the back of the wardrobe. I knew that I was going to be very selective at the London Back Show, as hiring the Mobiliser was still top of my agenda.

I'd never been to Olympia before so was unprepared for the size of the place. It was mid-day by the time I'd got there by train and underground and I was astonished to see hordes of fit looking young men pouring off the tube and into the building. Did all these people really have bad backs? I presented my ticket and was told "You've come to the wrong hall – this is the ski and snowboarding show." That explained a lot. My ski-ing days were over – beside all this testosterone-fuelled manhood I felt decidedly rickety and positively antique. I was told to go to the hall round the corner, where I presented my ticket again. "This is the wrong hall," I was told again; "This is the vet show." Well maybe animals get bad backs but a vet show wasn't going to help me. "How many halls are there?" I was beginning to get fed up. "Oh there are loads, but you are nearly there – it's the next one along." It was and it even said "Back Show" on a large sandwich board outside.

There was so much to see and I used every moment of my time over the two days trying out all kinds of gadgets, listening to lectures, watching and taking part in workshops. These included Pilates, Alexander Technique, and the Sarah Key method of decompression – the good old back block and rocking knees routine. I spoke to Sarah Key herself, who made me get down on the floor in front of her and use the back block there and then, despite my protestations of possibly still having ligament problems. "It's nearly always muscles, not ligaments causing the pain," she said firmly. *Nearly always, possibly, but not always always. She couldn't know my back history.* "God, your back muscles are tight," her assistant said, only confirming her prejudice. There's no rule to say that you can't have weak ligaments *and* tight back muscles – indeed if you have the former you are almost certain to have the latter, as I knew to my cost. Back blocks were being sold that day for £35, – mine had cost a fiver from Angela. I resolved to go home and use it until I got the Mobiliser – if my back muscles were as tight as they said I had all the more need for it.

I went to a couple of lectures, including watching unflinchingly (to my own astonishment) as one of Britain's top back surgeons – I'm sure he was the man whom Dr Pearson had called "the surgeon's surgeon" – showed slides of horrendously crooked and damaged spines and the nuts and bolts he'd put in to fix them, as well as the blood and gore of the actual operations. How grateful I felt that my back problem was nowhere near as bad as those he had illustrated!

A long queue of people desperate to speak to him formed as soon as his talk was over.

I tried out all sorts of interesting, not to say wacky back aids. There were all kinds of special chairs and supports that you attached to chairs. There were devices called inversion tables that turned you upside down with the aim of stretching out the spine. There was also the Flexibak, a set of wooden "ribs" which you lay in and sort of wobbled about in to massage your muscles – it looked like something a palaeontologist might have dug up. There were also some wonderful boots for safe exercising called Kangoo Jumps with a kind of curved runner on the bottom. I didn't buy them then, but succumbed and ordered some a fortnight later.

If there was one message I should take away from all of this, I thought, one key thing to remember, to make the whole visit worthwhile, was this: **backs need to be kept moving.** Backs were made to move, not to be slumped all day over computers (she writes, slumped over her computer). For all that, I felt that the back show was mainly about *backs* – spines and back muscles – and hardly a word about back pain caused by *pelvic* instability or troublesome ligaments. I think I came across the words "sacroiliac joint" once. I knew that a lot of my pain had come from my pelvis, still holding up well after the prolo injections there, but it hadn't been the answer to everything, otherwise I wouldn't be there.

Late in the second day I came across a smiling Lithuanian, oozing Baltic charm. He produced a lumbar corset similar to the one I was wearing and said, "You have one like zees? Rubbish belt, two dollars in China – srow in bin!" He then produced and fitted round my waist a substantial looking affair to which he attached a bicycle pump. He then inflated air pockets in the belt and pumped them up till I looked like the Michelin man. I felt ridiculously stupid, but boy was it comfortable. I could literally feel it lifting and separating out my vertebrae. That had to be worth having. He had all the literature "proving" that it worked. So, gulping at the price, I bought it and after returning home wore it proudly round the house for a day or two and had NO BACK PAIN! So I went and tried it out in the garden, which was where I really needed a belt, and it was then that I discovered its drawback – yes there had to be one. I knelt down to do some weeding and the belt rode up. I pulled it down. It rode up again. I went back into the house and pumped it and pumped it till it was so tight I could hardly breathe. I went back to my weeding, but still it rode up. When it had reached my boobs I abandoned it in disgust and put my old cloth one back on again. It felt like an old friend.

Two days later I drove to Bristol and returned with a hired Mobiliser, which Ed set up in the spare room for me. I didn't want to do it myself – I knew I'd put my back out! I put a CD player alongside, and prepared myself to work through all my CDs from Albeniz to Wagner. It was now late October and I had the Mobiliser on hire for four months. Time enough to tell what it could do for me. And I made a promise to myself that I would use only this machine and not have any other treatments throughout the winter months – a promise I kept until February.

I suppose you could call the Mobiliser, or Mobi, as the company calls it, a gadget. But it is a gadget apart. There is absolutely nothing else like it. As you lie on it fifty-six mechanical "thumbs" roll up and down underneath you, mobilising and separating out the spinal vertebrae whilst giving a deep massage to all your muscles from your calves up to your neck. It's like a Mexican Wave up and down your body. Even better, it has a heated pad inside the mattress, which feels just wonderful – comforting and spoiling and luxurious. The standard routine is to use the machine on the fifteen minute default setting, which works on the whole body, every morning and evening, and I followed this routine to the letter for at least the first month. It's a bizarre experience but one that I found I grew to really like. It was like Angela's foot mobilisation, all my massage therapists and Cindy walking on my bum all rolled into one. No need to go back now to any of these people. I was going to save money in the long run. And it was all under my own control.

Most importantly it worked, although it was hard going initially. As with all treatment or management programmes it was a long-term thing and miracles were not expected, but my back felt much more flexible after the first week. After a month I could touch my toes, something I hadn't done for over five years. I even turned over and lay on my tummy, but you're not supposed to do that so you didn't hear me say it. Using a different setting of lower body programme only, I did myself no harm and got a really good massage on my quads and iliotibial band.

As my back pain improved and my muscles became more supple I returned to using the exercise bike and doing core stability work and also some stretching. I would get through the winter like this and hopefully not lose fitness, the fitness I had fought so hard to achieve so that I could get back to walking in the spring. I know I said I'd stop walking after returning from Exmoor in September, but you didn't really think I meant it did you?

It was another cold winter with the snow coming even earlier and lasting even longer than the previous year. We had fun and games with the boiler again, and with frozen pipes, but the upside was that we also had a great time sledging on Christmas Day.

By the end of January 2011 I was beginning to think about whether I would send the Mobi back or bite the bullet and buy one. Although it was a wonderful aid it had not fixed all of my problems. I still had the spondylolisthesis – the forward slippage of L4 – and leg pains – soreness, burning, pricking – pains that could keep me awake at night. Now that I'd started seriously on machines I began to think about what else might be worth trying. The world now seemed to be full of gadgets and gizmos for "curing" pain. Might there still be something else that would actually finally heal me, rather than just manage things? I had come across something called SCENAR at the Back Show, claiming amazing results. I had kept it at the back of my mind ever since. By this time you'll have sussed me out – if there was something out there that might work I wanted to try it. Meanwhile, what was that pelvic pain that I could no longer deny was there – were my SIJs playing up again? Should I have a prolotherapy "top-up"?

All these thoughts were going around in my head when out of the blue towards the end of January Dr Pearson's secretary rang me to clear up an administrative matter. Having dealt with her query I then said, "I'd been thinking of ringing you anyway. I've been wondering about seeing Dr Pearson again for some more prolotherapy." "You'd better hurry up," she replied, "He's retiring in the middle of March." This was perhaps not surprising news, though unwelcome to me. Dr Pearson had been the person I'd turned to for nearly two years, and although I hadn't seen him since October I knew he'd always been there at the end of a phone. Calculating quickly I realised I could just get three prolotherapy sessions in before his retirement date, so I booked them up then and there.

"The Mobiliser is brilliant," I told Dr Pearson at the first session of my final series.

"Then why are you here?" he asked, but with a smile.

"Because it's not a cure, it's only helping to manage things."

I said I thought my pelvic ligaments were weak again and I wanted some more prolo. He agreed to inject the sacroiliac joints but not the L4 area – "it didn't work last time so I'm not going to pursue that." Perhaps it was just as well, remembering how my back had flared up in Scotland the previous summer.

The first injection into the right SIJ hurt quite a bit and he said that if the ligaments there were really strong I wouldn't feel it. By the time I got to the third injection a month later, however, he was saying, "There are some good solid ligaments there." He then gave me some statistics, in answer to my question about how many people were helped by prolotherapy. There was a percentage, he said who were helped permanently – who disappeared and were never seen again – a percentage who weren't helped at all, and a percentage who had treatments that lasted between six months and a year, and then needed it re-done. Which category, I wondered, did I fall into? As he was winding up the business he gave me the name of another doctor colleague of his who would be able to help me if I wanted to have top-ups in the future. Probably I would need it, though I didn't want to need it – I was really rather fed up of being stuck with needles.

This course of prolotherapy treatment answered one question for me anyway – what to do about the Mobiliser. I sent it back, this time by courier. Once I'd started prolo, deliberately inflaming my SIJs, the last thing I needed to do was aggravate them further by having the Mobi steam-roller over them.

I used the remaining time of my last sessions with Dr Pearson to bombard him with questions about my terrible legs. I must have driven him mad in those last few weeks. I had fibromyalgia, I said, I had trigger points, I had ITB syndrome, I had delayed onset muscle soreness. He scotched the idea of fibromyalgia, and said that the most likely cause was that the spondy in my back was compressing a nerve, which would cause this leg pain. He also gave me ITB stretches, different from any I'd been given before which seemed to help a bit.

My time with him was coming to an end. I turned up at the last session with a purple ankle. I'd decided I didn't have enough pain I said, so I'd caught my foot on the door frame going from the hall into the porch at home, turned my ankle over and fallen flat on my face spraining my ankle badly. He did not laugh.

Dr Pearson was busy over those last few weeks, seeing patients back to back (ha, ha!) and winding the business up. Opportunities for additional conversation were short. I managed to squeeze one last question in – had he heard of

SCENAR? No he hadn't, but as usual he sounded open-minded about anything that was out there that might help. I would see how I went with these latest injections, and then possibly pursue SCENAR in my own time, I decided. But that really would be the last thing I'd try. If that failed then I would buy a Mobi and manage my problem for the rest of my life.

Dr Pearson admitted that he hadn't been able to solve all my problems. One of the last things he said was, "It's very difficult to tell with you how much of your pain is coming from your SIJs and how much from your lumbar spine." Indeed. *You can cure some of the problems all of the time,* I thought, *and you can cure all of the problems some of the time, but you can't cure all of the problems all of the time.*

There was no doubt, though, that he had helped me enormously, particularly in the matter of diagnosis. He had always listened to what I had to say, some of which was probably a bit strange as I struggled to verbalise my pain, and had never dismissed anything I said, however bizarre. His injections had been given with care and skill and of course it was he who had referred me to Professor Green with the positive outcome for my hip. I had been coming to see him at various intervals for two years. In the middle of March I said a final grateful goodbye to him and went on my way, on my own once again.

CHAPTER 17

A High-Tech Solution

InterX

Three weeks after leaving Dr Pearson I finally got some improvement in my painful legs one night – a sleepless night in which I was being driven mad by the tingling, pricking and burning in my thighs – by curling up and rocking my knees to my chest, a standard sciatica exercise. At last some of the symptoms reduced, which told me that they were definitely caused by trapped/compressed/pinched (whatever is the correct term) nerves. I developed a programme of rocking and rolling for relieving the nerve pain *and* also doing ball massage on my ITB just in case that was also part of the problem. It was hard work and not always successful. It was time to play my last card – SCENAR – and see what it had to offer. If this didn't help, at least I had a better idea of how to manage things. Could SCENAR improve or even get rid of the spondy, which was probably – as Dr Pearson had suggested – causing the nerve problem and hence the leg pain?

SCENAR stands for Self Controlled Energy Neurone Adaptive Regulation, which doesn't exactly trip off the tongue, I'll admit. It was first developed in Russia for their space programme, which causes a few raised eyebrows when you mention it. But I'd learned to be open-minded. Few people had heard of prolotherapy or myofascial release either, but – apart from the hip surgery – they had been the most helpful of all the treatments I had tried. I would try SCENAR if I thought there was even a cat in hell's chance that it would do any good.

I had actually tried a "Pain Genie", an example of a SCENAR device, for five minutes at the London Back Show, because its claims to cure pain had been one of the reasons I'd gone there in the first place. Had it worked? Of course not. I didn't expect anything to cure five years of pain in five minutes. I'd remained curious about it and over the winter I'd begun to read up everything I could find about it and other SCENAR devices. More and more people seemed to be training to use them it seemed – physios, chiropractors, massage therapists, even doctors, although it was definitely mainly in the "alternative" camp. The list of testimonials and positive comments on forums from people who had been "cured" from seemingly awful pains and injuries was growing – surely all these people weren't making it up? One guy questioned it, mockingly and got the response from another chap who'd clearly been in severe pain, "I don't care if it's made by Chinese peasants, this thing bloody works." Right, I thought, I've got to try it.

The advice I was picking up was that I should find a therapist trained in using the device before forking out money to buy one. Also I was finding that many practitioners were moving on from SCENAR to a device called InterX. I couldn't find out exactly why, but there must be good reasons for it. There was very little general information about InterX though.

What I did find was that nearly all the practitioners of both SCENAR and InterX had trained with someone called Dr Zulia Valeyeva-Frost, who, it seemed, was one of the pioneers in the field and one of the leading practitioners in the world. Did she have a website? Where was she based? I suspected it would be Russia, or perhaps somewhere in America.

I found Dr Frost's website. I read her cv, which said among other things that she was recognized as the leading clinician and trainer in InterX technology. And then I found myself staring open-mouthed at the bottom of the page which told me simply that Dr Frost's practice was based in Cheltenham, Gloucestershire.

I picked my jaw up from off the floor and sent her an email quicker than you can say Self Controlled Energy Neurone Adaptive Regulation. It was the end of March.

Within two days she had replied. We then had an email conversation which, summarised, went something like this:

Me: *I have spondylolisthesis – can InterX do anything about it?*
Zulia: *Your condition is a serious one and to be honest I cannot give you a straight answer. Suggest course of treatment and relevant exercises – come and have consultation – I can refer you to local therapist – you'll need to buy own equipment and have a lot of treatments.*
Me: *Thanks for honest reply – my slippage not too severe – I'm going on holiday soon – you are my local therapist.*
Zulia: *Brilliant – would like to work with you after Easter – I am sure we can make a difference.*

So that was how it was left at the beginning of April. By the middle of April my rocking and rolling and ITB self-massage programme had paid dividends and my legs were beginning to feel like normal legs. With my pelvis firming up from the last three prolo sessions and my sprained ankle forgotten about (oh, if only the rest of me had healed so easily!) I had high hopes that I might be able to enjoy the group walking holiday we had booked for ourselves at St. Ives. I had calculated that an organised walking holiday would happily occupy Ed and that if I couldn't walk St. Ives would have plenty to offer me and I could enjoy the company of the group in the evenings. I was feeling slightly wary about it, as always when going on holiday, but if nothing else I had plenty of books to read and would enjoy having my meals cooked.

As it turned out I had another window, as good as my Viennese window. I walked four days out of a possible five, and suffered no ill effects other than blisters. I wore my lumbar corset and used my walking poles and I know both helped enormously, but I'm sure that February's prolo, a couple of recent sessions of myofascial release with Jill and the assiduous stretching I did before and after walking also contributed to making it all possible.

That week was the hottest April week in years. We had glorious weather every day and the scenery was spectacular. We walked along the stunningly beautiful coast paths often besides banks and fields carpeted with bluebells; we gazed across the sea with its ever-changing subtle colours observing bobbing seals and various birds through binoculars. In St. Ives holidaymakers flocked to the beaches and swam in the sea as if it was August. It was so hot sunscreen and sunhats were the order of the day and the ice-cream vendors were doing a roaring trade. All most peculiar for April as I can remember Easters when it has poured with rain, blown howling gales or even snowed.

Once home it was into the garden in a big way. Gardening, even with a lumbar corset, still gave me a lot of back pain and painful legs. Basically things were fine if I stayed upright, which perhaps was why walking was OK. But life requires you to do a lot of things that aren't upright and so I got in touch with Zulia Frost again to see what InterX could offer.

It was towards the end of May when I saw Zulia for the first time. One of the first things she said was that the InterX worked by stimulating the body's own healing mechanisms and that healing worked through inflammation, repair and remodelling of tissues. Now where had I heard that before? Yes – prolotherapy! This felt like familiar ground. The next good thing about the device is that it takes readings – don't ask me what of, I've never quite got the hang of this bit. But from the readings the device tells the therapist where to treat. The higher the number, the more work is needed in any particular spot.

Zulia took readings from all over my back and they ranged from 24 to 170. The "normal" figures tend to be in the range of 30-35. It seemed there was a lot to do. One of the big surprises to me was the high readings in my upper back and neck area, because this wasn't where I felt the pain. Zulia wasn't surprised – she said it was often the case in people with lumbar pain. The upper back muscles tighten to compensate for the lower ones. She moved her device over the whole of my back and pelvis and when it found a real hot spot it kind of got stuck and took a while before it could release. I gradually learned to think of my "sticky bits" as the really bad places.

The treatment was not at all unpleasant. It was a similar sensation to a TENS machine, although the device works very differently from a TENS. Zulia concluded the session with treatment on trigger points either side of my neck, which resulted in a typical "twitch" response but a very strong one – a very big involuntary tic. It wasn't painful, but I did wonder if my head was about to fall off!

The proof of the pudding would be in the eating, of course. This was a Tuesday and I didn't notice much reaction as the day wore on but Wednesday was different. I woke up very sore and stiff in my lumbar spine and sacroiliac joints and did a few gentle stretches to get me going. By lunch-time I had NO PAIN anywhere. I had a second session with Zulia on Thursday in which she did similar InterX work and also gave me infra-red laser treatment through what looked like electronic acupuncture needles into the L4 area. This was hi-tech stuff indeed. On Friday I was stiff and sore in lots of places, but on Saturday I again had NO PAIN in my SIJ or lumbar spine, despite helping Ed to move a compost bin and to lay a carpet. This therapy I decided was turning out to be some kind of minor miracle.

By Monday however the pain had returned. Was it because of the weekend activity? Or was this to be expected as a normal part of the treatment? I had two more treatments that week which calmed things down, and then Zulia went away on holiday giving me advice on how to self-treat with a device she lent me. This was a disappointment because I couldn't get it to work properly. But I'd had enough treatment from Zulia to get dramatic results. Over the next few weeks I became sore in every painful place I knew I had and quite a few I didn't.

My left shoulder for example. It was all to do with the muscle imbalance in my back, which the machine was trying to correct. It was, it seemed, addressing the scoliosis which Dr Pearson had mentioned almost in passing but which Zulia thought was a significant part of my pain. It was one hell of a powerful piece of technology, and I really wanted to believe in its powers.

Ironically, since I'd started on this course I saw two telly reports which basically said – I paraphrase – that electronic stimulation could make the lame walk and the blind see. "Well", said Ed, when I pointed this out to him, "To make the blind see probably cost about a million quid." Well – yes.

The soreness I was enduring made me a bit despondent when I went back to Zulia towards the end of the month. She told me to be patient. She thought there was improvement and that a chronic condition would not undo itself over night. She wanted me to do wall flattening exercises to improve my posture – I knew all about these since my days with Christine – and she showed me an extension to the exercise. I was to stand flat against the wall and slowly lift my arms in an arc till my fingers met at the top above my head.

Two days later whilst doing this "Sun" exercise at home and feeling good about it I put my hand behind my back and felt my spine. Was it my imagination, or had my L4 lifted back into place? And I had to admit that I had less leg pain now. So had this magic machine cured my spondylolisthesis and were the nerves no longer trapped? Zulia was to tell me over and over again, as had Dr Pearson, that my leg pain was coming from compressed nerves in my back but, although I believed them both and the many books I'd read, I still found it hard to get my head round this. I still persisted in thinking that if I'd got a pain in my legs then it was my legs that must be treated.

July came and I chalked up my sixth year of chronic pain. I went to climb over "my" stile. It's actually on one of my favourite walks which I do quite often, but it's a kind of ritual on July 6th. The stile had been mended rather poorly after I'd first reported it way back in July 2006 and had deteriorated badly again this year. I had reported it again and this time it had been fixed superbly well. The old one had been completely replaced with a new structure, firmly embedded in the ground. It had two tiers and a gritted surface providing a strong grip on the treads. It was the King of Stiles and was now a positive pleasure to climb over. So here I was on July 6th, five years later approaching it with pleasure, but what's this I see? The rusty old gate beside it, padlocked for all these years, is now undone, off its hinges and flung back against the fence leaving a wide gap that armies could march through. No need for any stiles now, rickety or new. I didn't know whether to laugh or cry.

Unexpectedly I received an email from the Mobiliser company; Mobiliser prices were going up but I, as a previous hirer, could buy one at the old price if I ordered before the end of the month. I ummed and aahed for three days. I had loved the Mobi, but it was a big bulky object and very expensive. I drew up a table with "Reasons to Buy" on one side and "Reasons not to Buy" on the other. I came up with eight in the first column and only two in the second. I checked my bank balance, gritted my teeth and placed an order for an ex-hire model late on 31st July. Would use of it interfere with InterX? Or might it complement it?

As July turned into August I worried again that InterX treatment, both from Zulia and from another self-treatment InterX device which she loaned me, was aggravating pain more than it was helping it. Zulia said that this was all part of the body's reaction to neurostimulation. Scoliosis and the muscle imbalance associated with it would take a while to correct. This was, she said, a harder problem to treat than my SIJ problem, but she remained confident that we were on the right track. I couldn't help feeling a bit down, though. If I'd had InterX treatment after one or two years instead of six, if I hadn't already had fifteen prolotherapy injections that aggravated pain I might feel differently. I wasn't sure what to tell Zulia when I saw her for the last time before going away for a three-week tour of Switzerland and Italy.

I had dared to risk booking another holiday abroad, with all the associated worries and anxieties about coping far from home. I survived it quite well, although I never put myself through anything as strenuous as the Alpine walking I'd done three years previously. Our first week was an organised rail tour of Switzerland and it was beautiful. The weather was mostly fine, the scenery fantastic and I had no trouble with sitting for hours at a time on a succession of scenic train journeys. In Italy we were on our own and spent the first four nights in the north, staying in Padua with day trips to Verona and Venice. Then we went for a further week into Tuscany, where we visited Florence and Lucca from our base in Montecatini, before flying home from Pisa.

August is the craziest time to go to Venice and Florence. They were crowded beyond imagining and it was unbelievably hot – some days the temperature soared to 42 degrees. Nonetheless if it's the only time I'll go to these cities I'm glad I've been.

My legs ached from so much standing whilst sight-seeing, but otherwise my body behaved remarkably well. Looking back, I decided that, although the aggravation and stimulation of pain had been hard to take over the previous couple of months, the InterX had played no small part in enabling me to have a relatively pain free holiday.

Back in grey old England my Mobiliser arrived. Joyfully I set it up and started to use it. Almost immediately I felt relief. Although I continued to have certain aches and pains throughout September and October I became convinced that my L4 was now free and no longer making a "step". It seemed to me that Angela's diagnosis three years previously of a "jammed in" L4 made as much sense as spondylolisthesis. Or were they the same thing? In any case "jammed in" didn't sound as scary as something with a long medical name, because it could become unjammed, as it now seemed that it had. I suspect it was the InterX that had done it, rather than the Mobi, but I shall never really know.

And then a really big blow. Feeling hopeful about things I had resumed my rocking and rolling exercises and core stability work until November when I had a flare-up in my least favourite place – my pubic symphysis. Bugger, bugger, bugger. I had trouble with it for the next two months. My spirits took a nose-dive – nothing in the world could send them as low as this could. I wondered if the Mobi was aggravating my pelvic joints and was depressed because I loved the massage it gave to my muscles and was reluctant to give it up. I was using it unsupervised and simply didn't know whether it was good or bad for me.

Just when I was at my lowest ebb at the beginning of December an email arrived from Zulia asking how I was and wanting feedback as it had been three months since I'd seen her. I replied rather negatively that I was full of aches and pains; that I'd had a flare up of pelvic pain; that I managed things on a day to day basis with the Mobiliser and my lumbar corset and by living quietly. I didn't know what to think about the InterX, I continued, but I'd spent *thousands* over the last six years and was reluctant to put more money into it. I thanked her for asking after me, concluding with all sincerity that it was nice to be thought about.

Straight away a reply came back. My problem, she said, was INSTABILITY (her capitals) due to weak ligaments and unless I strengthened my back sufficiently I would be prone to re-injury. The InterX, she thought, had done a brilliant job for me in the summer but she hadn't expected I'd be pain-free for ever. She understood my frustration and suggested that I bought or rented a device and combined use of it with core stability exercises. I would always have a weakness, she said, concluding that she had other patients like me, whom she saw less and less as they managed to control their flare-ups with the InterX.

So that was it, from the horse's mouth. InterX was not by itself a magic cure. It had been naïve, and perhaps lazy of me, to imagine it would be. It was however a very sophisticated device and used alongside appropriate exercises might still be worth having as a powerful tool in my armoury. I'd said it was the last thing I was going to try and I meant it. I replied:

Dear Zulia,

You are not the first person to tell me that my issue is instability – of my lumbar spine AND my pelvis – but thank you for saying it again. It just reinforces what I've been previously told… I'd forgotten to tell you that I have started doing core stability exercises, because I DO know – from you and from others that I need to strengthen my back and abdominals…I have been doing them for about a month now. And they are helping, but I suppose I felt disappointed to have another flare-up…I have been given sheets of exercises to do in the past…some have caused flare-ups… After Christmas I will think about buying an InterX – I agree it would probably be the best long-term. But nothing till after Christmas! Thank you again for all your help.

So that was why on 15th December I visited Zulia and came home with a brand new personal InterX device!

There was something about the fact that Zulia had positively chased me, her zeal in promoting InterX which made me decide that I should give it another chance. I couldn't keep on borrowing machines from her. And she had said right at the beginning that I should buy my own device because I would need many treatments. I now had two toys which I could play with happily all winter. If the coming winter was anything like the last three I wouldn't want to stir from the house for about three months.

I didn't want to go near another therapist ever again. Where once I had relished treatments like an addict – with Danielle, Charlotte, Angela, Dr Pearson and others – I'd now had it up to here with them. I bet I'd had a treatment or procedure beginning with every letter of the alphabet. Actually, as I thought about it a bit more, I realised I had. I felt a poem coming on.

The Pain Relief Alphabet

A is for Acupuncture needles very fine,
B is for the Back Block, which opens up your spine.
C's for Core Stability which makes your muscles stronger,
D is for Doctors seen – I hope for not much longer!
E is for Electrodes of the pain-relieving TENS,
F's for FRP and helpful "pain-supporting" Friends*.
G is for the Gym where I got a little fitter,
H is for the Hospital, which tried to get me better.
I is for InterX and Imaging and Ice,
J's for Joint injections – these weren't so very nice.
K is for Kangoo Jumps – these are quite good for backs,
L's for Lumbar corset – gives the strength my body lacks.
M is for McTimoney, Massage and Medication,
N is for Needles placed with skill and dedication.
O's for Osteopathy for joint manipulation,
P's for Prolotherapy for ligament stimulation.
Q is for Questions asked – and God, I've asked a lot!
R is for Rolfing, which made me sore and hot.
S is for Surgery – I've had some on my hip,
T's for Trigger point massage – off the tongue this doesn't trip!
U is for Ultrasound to stimulate the tissues,
V's for Visualisation – this helps with many issues.

W is for Weeping when you've really had enough,
X is for X-ray – to look at inside stuff.
Y is for Yoga, with its breathing very deep,
Z is for zzz – at last some pain-forgetting sleep.
There are some other treatments, which I didn't name this time,
It's not that I've forgotten, but I couldn't find a rhyme,
I've gone right through from A to Z and still got chronic pain,
I'd better go back to the start and work right through again!

*from the forum on www.painsupport.co.uk

CHAPTER 18

An Unexpected Setback

Nothing to do with Backs

We spent Christmas at my daughter's – she had recently bought her first house – and New Year at a hotel house party in the Brecon Beacons. I failed to fix my latest flare-up with my personal InterX device or with exercises and wondered what to do, suspecting misalignment in my pelvis again. Dr Pearson had said ages ago that I shouldn't have any more manipulation so that ruled out Danielle and Angela. Eventually I went, despite my reluctance now to go to any practitioners, to a different local physio in February 2012. She had all kinds of other strings, including myofascial release, to her bow, so I felt she was worth a try. Her version of myofascial release, however, was very different from what I was used to and didn't, in the two sessions I had with her, seem to make any difference.

But unknowingly she contributed something. She told me I was wonky. I suppose I could have guessed that, but the fact that she'd said it, could actually see it when I walked, made me sit down and think. Then I consciously altered my gait and used the Mobi in a targeted way and – hey presto – within a few days my pelvis had settled and was no longer misaligned.

I had fixed my own wonkiness! This was definitely a triumph for the Mobi – I wasn't going to have to give it up. I stopped rocking and rolling, however, which I found from trial and error was causing the pain and aggravating the instability and had probably caused the misalignment in the first place – I don't know why since I'd done these exercises successfully before but mine not to reason why – and my pelvis stayed properly aligned. Not just for a bit, but right up to the time of writing. I hesitate to say for ever – I think that would be to court disaster – but with more hope than I'd had for several months I resumed a regime of core strengthening exercises, and then I got on with the business of living.

2012 was a busy year because we had builders in again, installing a bathroom into what had been a loft, which meant hours of planning and staying just one step ahead of them. I used the Mobi and InterX to manage whatever aches and pains I had. At first I tried to monitor things and see which I preferred but I was too busy and my pain levels not great enough to make it worthwhile. Use of both became rather haphazard and I survived perfectly well without the Mobi when it had to live in the garage for several months while the house was turned upside down.

And so the year went on. At the end of July I was back at Angela's clinic seeing a delightful young physio called Emma, to try and cure a new pain that had popped up on the inside of my knee after a ramble in March, and which I'd been trying unsuccessfully to cure ever since. Nothing I did could shift it. Not ibuprofen, nor InterX, nor ice, nor heat, nor the Mobi, nor trigger point massage, nor even sports massage with Steve – which in fact made it worse. Obviously I was targeting the wrong spot. "Find the pain," John Barnes says "and look elsewhere for the cause." It was extremely annoying because yet again my walking was hampered, though I ignored it as much as I could and refused to let it stop me going wherever I wanted. Walking, actually, was hindered much more by almost non-stop rain and oceans of mud everywhere, which became a permanent feature of the landscape for almost the whole of 2012.

Emma massaged and did ultrasound and told me to "beef up" my gluteal strengthening and stretch my hamstrings three times each, holding each stretch for thirty seconds. This was a completely different kettle of fish from my blink-and-you'll-miss-them stretches. I felt these ones, I *really* felt them. But I also felt improvement, and there's nothing like a hint of progress for encouraging me to continue.

Early August continued wet. The builders had nearly finished and teaching was over till September. I had nothing to do but lie on the floor and do my exercises, whilst watching the Olympics – where it seemed somewhat less wet – feeling motivated by the often inspirational athletes to work harder than ever to improve my body strength and suppleness as much as I could, especially after learning that Nick Skelton and Mary King won their equestrian medals despite having previously broken their necks. Talk about comebacks!

Memories of my early sessions with Angela came back when I visited Emma. I remembered her emphasis on stretching the whole body, in particular my quadratus lumborum muscles – the ones joining the ribs to the pelvis. I was terrified of stretching them. I'd restricted stretches to my legs which felt fairly safe. My lower back was sore again, surely there must still be something wrong with the ligaments? But Dr Pearson had said "There are some good strong ligaments there". Tentatively I sat on the coffee table and stretched my right elbow to my left knee as Angela had taught me. I couldn't reach it – Oh God I was tight there! I raised my left arm over my head and bent to the opposite side. That was even worse – was that tight fascia, shrink-wrapped around my ribs again? No wonder I had back pain if my sides were tethered. I did it again, a little stronger, then did every upper body stretch I could remember, dreading that within half-an-hour I'd be worse.

My ligaments did not complain. Nothing came out. My back actually felt better! The soreness across my lumbar area was easing for the first time for months. Was it really now all down to tight fascia and muscles? Maybe Sarah Key's words "It nearly always is tight muscles" were appropriate – *now*. The reason that things were going well, I decided, was that my pelvic ligaments (despite the little hitch over the previous winter) were much stronger and holding my pelvis firmly in place *and* because my spine now seemed to be in a much better condition. And it was prolotherapy and InterX which had finally got me there!

I got my personal InterX device out again, and my assortment of various balls. I stretched my fascia, I worked on muscles, I massaged my soft tissues and I stretched day after day. I hadn't done this seriously for months; in fact I couldn't remember when I'd last stretched my upper body. Definitely not whilst I was having all that prolotherapy, but I'd certainly done it, if only briefly, after seeing Ruth Duncan in 2010. Surely the whole of 2011 hadn't gone by without my stretching it? Whatever, I was pretty sure that it was a long time since I had done a sustained programme such as the one I was doing now and which was reaping benefits. Now I relished stretching every which way, and as British gold medals accumulated and the emotional temperature at the Olympics rose to fever pitch so did my spirits soar on my Pilates mat in front of the telly.

In fact the only pain that didn't go was the knee pain, although I did ease it – enough for me to be able to enjoy a wet walking week in the Peak District in late August. One day I walked nine miles, which was as much as I ever used to do *before* my injury. In September I upped my exercises and improved things even more. I had hours of pain-free time! In early October I went Scottish dancing and actually felt better after the evening's activity than before!

So why wasn't I celebrating, popping open the champagne and signing up for yoga classes?

Because I'd now got bowel cancer, that's why.

My first reaction was one of astonishment. Cancer? Surely not. Other people get cancer. I was first investigated for it after having a couple of unclear results from the bowel cancer screening test in July. Those of you over a certain age will be familiar with this. If you're under sixty I'll spare you the details – you have this treat in store. All I can say is, don't bin the test as I understand a large percentage of the population do – it could save your life. I wasn't unduly worried, thinking I'd probably got piles which I'd been prone to off and on for years, and went off to my Peak District holiday without any anxiety.

But cancer it was, proved by further investigations and the results of a biopsy in September. According to a CT scan though, it didn't appear to have spread beyond the one tumour, which I was told was in a good position to be removed by surgery, with a very high chance that that alone would cure me.

I was in total denial. Did I really have this dread disease? At least it had been caught early and the prognosis was good. My mother had been cured of bowel cancer in her eighties and lived, as we have seen, well into her nineties. Many people fight cancer and I would fight it too, although I was not sure that there would be a lot of fighting to do as surgery was a job I could leave to the professionals, who deemed me relatively "young" – how flattering! – and therefore a good prospect for a full recovery. I still found it hard to get my head round it though, because in September I felt in better physical shape than I'd done for the last seven years. I hadn't smoked for thirty years, I scarcely drank, I ate healthily, I exercised lots – I lived a healthy lifestyle. Why me? Why now?

All the nurses, doctors and administrative staff were falling over themselves to be nice to me and whilst I of course appreciated their kindness I couldn't help thinking, *you don't understand. I've had so much pain for seven years, and now I haven't got any, especially not where they're telling me I've got a nasty little lump growing.* That was why it was so hard to take in. I'd struggled for so long to rid myself of all the pains that the NHS hadn't managed to cure and now when all I had was an irritating little pain in my knee they were going to whip me in fast-tracked to operate on something I wasn't even aware of having. I was tremendously grateful they were but couldn't help feeling how puzzling it all was.

Hadn't I said that I knew the good old NHS would take good care of me if I ever got cancer? I still didn't seem particularly fazed by it. I'd had so many procedures done to my body in the last seven years that I felt I could deal with most things now. Also living with chronic pain for that length of time had resigned me to the idea that my body was slowly disintegrating. The great thing about surgery, at least, is that you go to sleep, someone else does all the work and when you wake up it's all been done.

I had a couple of months to wait before my scheduled operation date of November 12th, during which time I tried to keep as fit as possible before going into hospital. On November 11th, which was actually dry, even sunny for a change, Ed and I walked on Cleeve Common. As I stood gazing at the stunning view, which never ceases to amaze me, of the Severn Valley carpeted below, I wondered when I would next be here again. My gung-ho attitude of the last couple of months was fading, and I couldn't help feeling some anxiety at what was to follow. Having eight inches cut out from my guts and the remainder re-sectioned and then stapled back together sounded a lot less nice somehow than having my hip joint cleaned out.

I went into theatre at about 2.30 in the afternoon of November 12th. They woke me up about 6pm to tell me that the operation had gone well. But I never got beyond the recovery room. My blood pressure went down to my boots – way below the lowest it sank in Coventry – and not surprisingly I felt dreadful. Three hours later I was operated on again for suspected internal bleeding, just after I'd croaked that I wanted to die.

This time when I woke up I felt immediately better. One and a half litres of blood had been washed out of my abdominal cavity and I'd been given a transfusion of a similar amount. I'd psyched myself up for surgery that morning, but had never expected to have two operations in one day! This second one finished at approximately 11pm, at which point the surgeon resumed another operation he'd already started, finishing that one at about 12.30am and phoning Ed – who'd waited in the hospital from 7pm till nearly midnight to see me but had eventually gone home – at quarter to one. What a day for all concerned!

I was in Intensive Care when the surgeon visited me on Wednesday morning. I thanked him for saving my life. Perhaps this was rather dramatic as I'd been closely monitored in the Recovery Ward, which was routine procedure, and safely operated on a second time, but he did say it was the first time in eleven years of doing keyhole surgery that he'd had this problem. I still respected his excellent reputation. Either way he did save my life. Untreated cancer would have killed me slowly; bleeding to death would have done it rather quicker.

I spent two days in Intensive care. My arms were like dartboards from all the attempts to get a new cannula into my collapsing veins and I was so festooned with tubes that I felt as wired up as a telephone exchange, but I was alive, and, I realised, very glad to be. From now on I just had to follow instructions and leave it up to the body's own miraculous healing powers and I would get better.

I had blood taken daily and was given magnesium one day, potassium the next and phosphorus the next, in order to correct any mineral imbalance in my blood. I also had specially fortified drinks three times a day. That was all fine by me – at this rate, I thought, I'll go home healthier than when I came in.

After that I was transferred to a general ward where I made

a steady recovery and discovered that a wonderful side-effect of prolonged bed-rest and being stuffed full of pain-killers was that my knee pain had gone – for the time being anyway.

In the bed next to mine on the ward was Dorothy, a lady of 87 years. Robust and down-to-earth she had a wonderful sense of humour and cheered us all up. She'd had a nasty skin cancer on her leg removed and was now also recovering and ready to go home. "What's the weather like?" she asked me as I stood at the window on the morning of Monday 19th November, the day of my discharge and exactly one week on from being admitted "Blustery," I replied, "but not wet or frosty." It seemed quite a reasonable day actually for mid-November and I remembered that the previous day had been glorious. It's true I was only looking over a car park, but our ward was on the top floor of the hospital and there was a good view to the hills in the distance. Everything had been etched with a silvery frost at first and then a cheerful sun had come up brightening the whole world with autumn colours. At the edge of the car park was a group of birch trees which had not yet lost their leaves and which had shimmered as the sun caught them, like golden rain fireworks. *You see what you want to see,* I thought – *beautiful trees or a car park.*

"I always wake up every morning and think how glad I am to be alive," said Dorothy and then as if to echo my thoughts of the previous day, "I look at the trees and the flowers and thank God I'm still here. The trees and the flowers, what more do you want?"

"What a wonderful view to have of life!" I replied. And that was the thought I took home with me when Ed came to fetch me an hour or so later.

CHAPTER 19

Putting it Back Together

Gathering up the Threads

There's no doubt that my exciting time in hospital has served to concentrate my mind. I'm not ready to die, I realise, far from it. In fact with my health improving day by day I feel more and more ready to grasp life passionately by the throat. I've still got a million things to do before I finally pop my clogs at, hopefully, some advanced but not too senile age. I feel, of course, enormous gratitude not only to my surgeon whom I have thanked in person, but also to the unknown blood donors whom I will never know. "Keep it up," I said to a friend who donates regularly. "You really will be saving lives." And what of the poor chap who had his operation interrupted? Maybe one day I can track him down and thank him.

My convalescence went well. I paced myself, with all the knowledge that I had learned from Pain Management, and improved daily. Six weeks to the day from my last walk on Cleeve Common I walked there again, this time with my family who visited just before Christmas. I felt a quiet sense of satisfaction. I had been looking after myself sensibly and taking gentle walks when it wasn't raining, and now here I was in one of my favourite places managing a decent length walk with no problems at all. It boded well.

There was however one fly in the ointment – I was going to have to have chemotherapy. Six months of it. There was the smallest chance that, despite the success of the surgery, what they called a "cancer seedling" might have found its way into my bloodstream. A series of appointments has been booked with the first actual treatment starting on January 3rd 2013, so no time is being wasted. Maybe this is when my "fight" against cancer will really begin.

It's not that I want to trivialise cancer which is for many people the worst thing they will have to face. Cancer is often symptomless; it creeps up on you unawares. It devastates families, can cause enormous pain and suffering and is life-threatening. People die from cancer, including my own father who lived to eighty-five. Others die younger and often suddenly from too-late diagnoses, as happened to a friend who never lived to see his longed-for and carefully planned retirement. Many people do recover, but only after enduring a long fight involving unpleasant treatment. Some people write books about their own personal cancer stories, as a way of dealing with it – a kind of therapy. All of this is valid.

But when a friend said recently, "I was shocked to hear about your cancer. Of course I know you've had a lot of trouble with your back but that was trivial compared to this," it didn't really ring true for me. As far as I'm concerned my experience with my back, pelvis and hip has been far, far worse than my experience of cancer. My cancer was caught early and treated successfully with surgery, my after-care and post-operative pain management were excellent, my prognosis is good and I feel I've come through it all relatively unscathed. Despite having two operations on one day I remained upbeat in hospital, *because I knew that I had a good outcome and that I was going to get better.* Pain from the operation scars was relatively short-lived, a matter of weeks, rather than months or years.

However, I don't have any such expectations with my back and pelvis. Despite my euphoria in the summer I know that I have to keep up a daily regime of exercises to maintain myself in such a good condition. That has not been possible due to hospitalisation and post-operative scarring, and although I have now resumed some stretching I have a long way to go to get back to the relatively fit state I was in in the summer. I have too many twinges in too many places. Exercises for me have to be a lifetime commitment. For me cancer was a short-lived experience, but back pain has been with me for over seven years, sometimes very severe, and it is that that is my nemesis, not cancer.

Dr Pearson once asked me if I'd had any back trouble *before* the accident – he was, I think, the only person who asked this telling question. I told him I used to get very bad backache after gardening. I'd had it for years, actually, probably even going back to pregnancy. My standard method of treatment was two paracetamol and a hot bath, and I'd be fine the following morning. My mother had also complained of gardening backache for years and I'd assumed it was just something that happened as you got older. The fact that my father, who gardened passionately every weekend and every day after his retirement, never complained of such pains seemed to have passed me by. Clearly it wasn't a requirement of growing older. Far more likely was that my mother and I shared the same genetic make-up of the collagen in our ligaments and that she, like me, also had ligaments weakened by pregnancy. Unlike me, however, she had no accident to add insult to injury and her backache was restricted to post-gardening episodes. She didn't know about core-stability and hip strengthening exercises, but in her sixties she took up yoga – much less common then – and was to be found, lycra-clad on her bedroom floor, deep breathing and stretching every morning before breakfast. Did it help her back? It's too late to ask her now.

The summer of 2005 had been particularly demanding on my back, as I discovered that my new Gloucestershire garden soil seemed to consist entirely of Severn clay. I attacked it vehemently and kept up the paracetamol and hot baths until the day of the injury. Dr Pearson's theory, I think I'm right in saying, is that the forced abduction of the accident caused me to tear the hip cartilage and to over-stretch and/or tear *already weakened* ligaments. I may, he said, also have been hypermobile in my lumbar area. Before the injury I could not just touch my toes, I could put the palms of my hands flat on the floor. I thought it was a party trick and was rather proud of it. But hypermobility is not a party trick, it is a condition which makes injuries more likely and repairing them more difficult.

The subluxation (partial dislocation) of the pelvic joints, with all the attendant pubic symphysis and sacroiliac joint pain probably came on later as I struggled to walk, and the spondylolisthesis and scoliosis later still as a consequence of the poor mechanics in my pelvic/lower back region. This seems to me the most likely scenario, given that it was the groin that hurt first, and the back problems which came on later, but I'll never really know.

These mechanical problems then gave rise to all the myofascial problems – muscle spasm, trigger points, a straitjacket of fascial tension – with my loss of core stability only making matters worse.

How to do undo this history? If I'd known then what I know now! I'd have certainly done things in a different order. First I would have had the hip sorted. And then the pelvis. It seems sensible to go down the physio, chiropractic route for a bit – many people are helped this way. But once it became clear that manipulation wasn't working I'd have gone for prolotherapy to strengthen my ligaments much sooner. And I'd have had myofascial release – to relieve the muscular and fascial tension – at the same time as prolotherapy. I think that one of the reasons I had setbacks during my prolo treatments is that I had too many tight muscles pulling in the opposite direction from the ligaments which were trying to grow tighter. Sometimes I think that it's been an on-going struggle to get some bits of me to glue together and others to unstick…

Prolotherapy has definitely been a success story in stabilising my pelvis. It was less successful in dealing with the spondy. I had to wait till I'd discovered InterX before that was helped. How it has done it I shall never really understand, but I think it's something to do with stimulating the nerves to get the muscles to unspasm, and then the joints can resume their proper position by themselves. And with the spondy improved my leg pain has finally gone.

Prolotherapy, InterX and myofascial release – three very effective treatments. Yet who knows about them?

As I live out the dying days of 2012 I realise that I have come to the end of my quest. My body is far from perfect. There are too many back and pelvic twinges for that and I can only assume it's from muscles which tighten either because they are still weak or because there is still a certain amount of instability around the pelvic and iliolumbar joints. Maybe I belong to the category of patients that Dr Pearson said benefit from prolotherapy top-ups. I still have the phone number of the colleague he recommended and more than once have thought of contacting him. It may still happen, one of these days…

I've also worked out that my knee pain, which has inevitably returned, is being "referred" from tight bum muscles – probably that wretched piriformis again. I'm working on it with the Mobi, the rubber ball and stretches and am finally getting results – much better results than in the summer from stretching alone. No doubt there'll be other pains. In most cases I feel I now have the knowledge, and the equipment, to get on top of these myself and if I really can't I know a man – or woman – who can. I know lots of people – wonderful therapists all – who can. I never thought when I moved here that I would get to know the area not by its pubs and shops, but by its hospital and complementary treatment centres!

I dare to say that I've finally got the answers as to the *causes* of my pain and that I don't think there are any surprises left. The last of the Russian dolls has been exposed; the last symptoms to be improved – spondy and scoliosis – helped by the InterX, developed interestingly enough from Russian technology. Zulia herself said it wasn't going to cure my fundamental weakness and that I would always have to work at my strengthening and stretching exercises. But hopefully no more serious misalignments. No more symphysis pubis dysfunction, or sacroiliac joint dysfunction or torn hip cartilage, unless I'm very unlucky. No more surprises. Journey's end. There are no pain relieving treatments booked for 2013 and there is to be no 2013 "pain diary".

What of the future? First let's all hope that it doesn't rain as much next year. 2012 has been officially declared the second wettest year on record, which comes as no surprise. This time we weren't inundated in our part of Gloucestershire, but it's been dismal nonetheless, and my heart goes out to all the families we see almost nightly on the telly as their lives are devastated by the misery of flooding.

I'm under no illusions. I know I'll never be the person I once was and that I'll always have to take great care of my body. I intend to. I do not intend to bump it up and down on horses, cram it into uncomfortable positions in canoes or sailing boats, throw it around a tennis court or hurl it down ski slopes. I feel tremendously privileged that I've had the chance to do these things in the past. I've had great joy from such activities, and have many wonderful memories of them. But it's a bit of an irony that in all the years I rode – and fell off – horses as a child, and on all the ski-ing holidays I enjoyed, both as a child and an adult, I never injured myself once. Barely a scratch. And then I go on a summer stroll and turn myself into a semi-invalid for seven years, weakening my body possibly for the rest of my days. Isn't life strange, ridiculous even?

Nor do I intend to climb Kilimanjaro, take up bungee jumping or go white water rafting. Now I get joy from rambling, growing delphiniums and playing chamber music, all of which seem age appropriate and all of which I can do with very little pain. I am even – dare I say it – content a lot of the time to "potter."

Chemotherapy is not a joy to look forward to but, although I may have to eat my words in a few months' time, I don't think there's anything they can throw at me that will be as bad as pubic symphysis pain. Apart from the cartilage tear in my hip, which was a clear discrete injury, I believe that my misaligned unstable pelvis was the root cause of all my problems. Having read up about pelvises the following quote, from one of many websites, sums up perfectly what I have experienced:

"Pelvic pain is one of a kind. The pelvis needs to be stable to do everything – sitting, standing, walking, even sleeping! The structure and function of the pelvis is extremely complex, and if one little thing is out of alignment, then joints will move improperly, ligaments and tendons will develop tears, and the muscles of the lower back and buttocks will go into spasm. Few things are quite so debilitating, and few things are so poorly understood by the medical community".

When I think of the last seven years I sometimes think of the wasted hours and days spent lying around on sofas because to move at all felt too painful. If, on the other hand, I look at what I've achieved in those seven years *despite* having chronic pain then things don't seem quite so bad. This is when Positive Thinking is a good thing.

First and foremost I kept everything going for Mum in those first three years and managed I know to brighten her days on many occasions. I also kept my piano teaching business going and got all my students through their exams and some performing in the local festival. I performed myself in the same festival, eventually with a certain amount of success. I met other musicians who have become firm friends and with whom I now play duos, trios and duets. I managed a considerable amount of walking including climbing to the top of Cleeve Hill several times, the Malverns twice, part of Offa's Dyke, parts of the Cornish Coast Path and of course, my forays in the foothills of the Alps. I've managed two foreign holidays and several others in Britain. I've been to concerts and the theatre and family celebrations. Many times I've had to grit my teeth and certainly some of the occasions were considerably marred by pain, but here is the good thing: I have all the memories of these happy occasions, but not the memory of the pain. Which goes to show that it was worth struggling through the pain in order to have a life and create those memories, no matter how fraught with difficulties it sometimes was.

If all goes to plan my future could be relatively bright. But the future is always an unknown country and all we can do is plan for the best, but not be too surprised when it doesn't happen.

This has been my story. My story of back and pelvic pain. Not a straightforward one, I think you'll agree! Bodies are extremely complicated and not all pain has a cause that can be seen even with today's sophisticated technology. My total ignorance didn't help. I can name a few muscles and ligaments now and know approximately where they are, but I still feel I've only scratched the surface of understanding what they do and how they all work. Would I pass Grade 1 in anatomical knowledge, if there was such a thing? I've probably expressed myself very badly in many instances too – I'm sure, for example, there is a difference between a trapped nerve, a compressed nerve and a pinched nerve but I don't know it, and if I've got it wrong it's just too bad.

Everybody, not to say every body is different, and you have to find your own way through the maze; especially it seems with back pain. In some ways I was unlucky, because no-one could have expected to develop such a complicated set of symptoms from merely falling over a stile. In other ways I know I am extremely lucky – I have only to log in to the Pain Support forum to know how devastated some people's lives are by chronic pain, how severely they have suffered and continue to suffer, often for many more years than me and often with very little hope of improvement. Yet everybody out there is fighting – fighting for pain relief, fighting for a better quality of life, fighting – in many cases – benefit cuts, and fighting hardest of all for knowledge and understanding of the causes of their pain.

There's not a lot more to say really. I'm almost sorry I've come to the end. I first started writing this soon after attending the Pain Management Course. "Find new interests", they said – though I'm not sure this is quite what they meant. I was supposed to find interests that *stopped* me thinking about pain! But writing it *has* stopped me thinking about pain, because it has been a distraction. The challenge of marshalling my thoughts, choosing words, honing sentences and polishing paragraphs has been totally absorbing and an enormous pleasure – a totally unexpected pleasure. Finally seeing it all come together has given me great satisfaction.

It's not only been a therapy, it's been part of the cure. Reading through my pain diaries, extracting the relevant information and piecing together all the different strands of the story, combined with internet research helped me get things straight in my head. This then led me ultimately, albeit circuitously, to the correct diagnosis.

How glad I am that I did keep fighting, that I didn't accept things, that I did keep going until I got answers as to the *cause* of my problems and tried out all the treatments that might possibly be of help. If I hadn't I might still be curled up on the sofa hardly able to move.

I've been lucky in that I've had the money and the time to pursue things. I've had a wonderful lot of therapists. I remember them with inordinate gratitude and affection, which I hope shines through in the writing, and am rather sad that I'll probably never see most of them again.

Despite all their help it hasn't been a simple journey. In the end, it was I who had to put it all together. It was my persistence that finally won through and gave me my life back.

And I'm a little bit proud of that.

Afterword

At the end of March 2013, halfway through my chemotherapy regime I was sent at one of my regular hospital appointments to have a routine blood test. Normally I would have had it done by the practice nurse at my GP's surgery the previous day, but this particular week my aunt's funeral had prevented that. "Where do I go?" I asked the oncology nurse who'd handed me the blood form. "Just follow Mr Thingy" (her words), "I've just explained it to him." Mr Thingy was a tall slim man, possibly of a similar age to me, with greying hair, glasses and a kind smile. By the time we had trekked down innumerable corridors and reached the other side of the hospital we had struck up a conversation. In the waiting area for the phlebotomist we had to take numbers on cards from a hook on the wall. He took two and handed the first to me. "That's very gentlemanly of you," I said and took a seat opposite him.

Our conversation continued and it turned out we'd both had bowel surgery from the same surgeon. "It was quite exciting when I had it actually," I said. "They had to open me up again three hours after the first operation and give me a blood transfusion because I had internal bleeding. Our surgeon interrupted someone else's operation to come and save my life."

"That could have been me," he replied. "I was told that

my operation was interrupted and put on hold for something like that."

"On November 12th?"

"Yes."

I stared at him. All I could say was "Wow!" And then, "you know I really wanted to meet you and thank you for your part in saving my life – and here you are."

He leant forward, grasped my hand and shook it warmly. I asked him his name, he told me and then I told him mine, and reiterated my thanks. We shook hands again, all the time beaming at each other. He then told me of his illness, symptoms and treatment regime which sounded a lot worse than mine and I wished he hadn't had to have that extra burden of a delay in his operation – his second operation for cancer within a few months – and I expressed this. Once more he grasped my hand and we smiled wordlessly at each other. And I reflected that it probably felt as good to him to meet the person whose life he had helped save as it did for me to meet the man who had helped save it.

Then my number was called and I went in for my blood test, after which he went in for his and we parted company. I may see him again in the oncology department waiting area, or I may never see him again. It doesn't matter – a niggling matter has been given closure, and in the nicest possible way. I am still gobsmacked though. Over 250 people pass through Cheltenham oncology department every week and yet here I was meeting, by pure chance, the one person I'd wanted to meet for four months.

And all because I went to a funeral on a certain Tuesday and broke my usual pattern for blood tests.

Acknowledgements

I am extremely grateful to all my wonderful practitioners for their treatments, and for the insights and education in matters anatomical they gave me which enabled me to progress towards recovering my health, especially: Melanie Whittle, Gabrielle Swait, Karen Jenkins, Dr James de Courcy, Adrian Lyster, Nina Callender, Wendy Zhao, Caroline Body, Rosy Adams, Cheltenham Pain Management Team, Caroline Spearing, Pam Lear, Jane Breen-Turner, Ann Hackett, Karen Pare, Julie Austin, Dr Chris Parsons, Professor Damian Griffin, Ruth Duncan, David Tabrizi, Dr Zulia Frost and Mr Neil Borley.

A big thank you to my friends Moira and Gordon Mott, for their helpful comments on the manuscript, and for their hospitality. I am indebted also to my brother Tony Irvin for his encouragement and his invaluable advice on all aspects to do with publishing and marketing.

I am immeasurably grateful to Ed for his proof-reading, his contributions to the text and artwork, and for his seemingly unlimited forbearance and support throughout the last seven years.

Finally my thanks to those at Matador who have been involved in the publishing process, especially Terry Compton for the cover design and Jennifer Liptrot for her helpful advice and support throughout.

References

Chapter 1

The Times Complete Family Health, Dr Michael Apple, Dr Jane Collins (Hamlyn – 2001).

(No longer available, but there are plenty of similar books which are).

Chapter 4

The Trigger Point Therapy Workbook, 2nd edition, Claire Davies NCTMB with Amber Davies NCTMB, foreword by David G Simons MD. (New Harbinger Publications Inc. 2004).

(My blue "Bible").

Chapter 5

Sciatica Solutions, Loren Fishman and Carol Adman (W.W Norton and Co).

(Excellent text on sciatica and piriformis syndrome).

Treat your own Back, Robin McKenzie (Spinal Publications New Zealand Ltd 1981).

Chapter 9

Back Sufferers' Bible, Sarah Key (Vermilion).

CHAPTER 10

Fibromyalgia and Chronic Myofascial Pain, 2nd edition, Devin Starlanyl, Mary Ellen Copeland (New Harbinger Publications Inc. 2001).

(My green "Bible").

CHAPTER 12

The Multifidus Back Pain Solution, Jim Johnson (New Harbinger Publications Inc.)

(Exercises for strengthening the multifidus – an important back "stabilising" muscle).

The Secret Cause of Low Back Pain, Vicki Sims PT (SI Press 2004).

(Small but comprehensive text on sacroiliac joint pain, available from www.sidysfunction.com).

OTHER USEFUL BOOKS

The Concise Book of Muscles, Chris Jarmey (Lotus Publishing 2003).

(Excellent pictures, short, clear text – wonderful as a basic education in muscle anatomy).

Manage your Pain, Dr Michael Nicholas, Dr Allan Molly, Lois Tonkins, Lee Beeston (Souvenir Press 2003).

(One of the best books for Pain management).

FOR MYOFASCIAL RELEASE

A Patient's Guide to Understanding John F Barnes' myofascial release, Cathy Covell (2009).

Myofascial Stretching, a guide to self-treatment, Jill Stedronsky,

Brenda Pardy (Aardvark Global Publishing Company LLC 2006).

Resources

Numerous websites have sprung up since I first started my research. Here is just a sample of some I've found particularly useful.

PAIN

www.painsupport.co.uk

A wonderful site run by Jan Sadler who herself has chronic pain but seems to be upbeat, **all the time**. She was recently awarded an MBE for her fantastic work.

www.painclinic.org

Run by a retired consultant in Pain Management – useful information on many issues, including prolotherapy.

SPORTS INJURIES

www.sportsinjuryclinic.net
www.sportsinjurybulletin.com

MYOFASCIAL RELEASE

www.myofascialrelease.com

(American website of John F. Barnes).

www.myofascialrelease.co.uk

(British website of Ruth Duncan).

ROLFING

www.rolfing.org
www.rolfinguk.co.uk

PROLOTHERAPY

www.caringmedical.com
www.prolotherapy.org
www.bonesdoctor.com/prolo.html
www.bimm.org.uk
(Website of British Institute of Musculoskeletal Medicine with list of Prolotherapy practitioners in UK).

BACK PAIN AND MOBILISER

www.backcare.org.uk
www.backinaction.co.uk

PELVIC PAIN

www.pelvicpain.org.uk
Pelvic Pain including sacroiliac joint dysfunction and symphysis pubis dysfunction.

INTERX AND SCENAR

www.interxclinic.com
www.scenartherapist.co.uk
The clearest site I have found for this device, though there are many others.